SHADE AND ORNAMENTAL
TREES
IN COLOR

SHADE AND ORNAMENTAL
TREES
IN COLOR

WILLIAM FLEMER, III

Foreword by Brian O. Mulligan

GROSSET & DUNLAP, INC.
Publishers, New York

PRUNUS BLIREIANA

Published Simultaneously in Canada
Library of Congress Catalog Card Number: 65-21502
Manufactured in the United States of America
by SWEENEY, KRIST AND DIMM

CONTENTS

To my parents, who first kindled my interest in
trees and encouraged me to write about them,
this book is affectionately dedicated.

THE INDESCRIBABLE BEAUTY OF FLOWERING CRAB APPLES DECORATE THIS
SPRING LANDSCAPE. See pages 43-46

THIS STREET PLANTING OF EVERGREEN CHINESE ELMS CAST POOLS OF WELCOME SHADE ON A SUMMER DAY. Ulmus parvifolia sempervirens. See page 73

FOREWORD

Books dealing with the selection and care of suitable trees for our parks and gardens, when written by competent authorities, are always welcome. They provide sound advice, especially for the constantly increasing number of new suburban home owners, on what kinds of trees to choose for a particular climate and situation, how to plant and prune them, what pests or diseases they may be liable to, how large they will grow, and so on.

Mr. Flemer's new book does all this for us and more. By dividing his trees into four classes—deciduous, broad-leaved evergreens, conifers and palms—then again by size, those less than and those more than forty feet in height, he makes it easy to select those of the type and size required, instead of having to hunt through lengthy lists of catalogues. The chief features of each tree mentioned are then briefly described without botanical details—the foliage, flowers, fruit, hardiness and size—to provide an adequate overall picture of its appearance and capabilities.

There is a good choice in the smaller deciduous trees, which are so important nowadays, especially in crab apples, cherries, hawthorns and some other excellent individual species. Most of the broad-leaved evergreens, however, are only suitable for the south or warmer parts of the Pacific Coast—which is to be expected with this group. The same applies to an even greater degree to the palms.

Of large deciduous trees almost sixty are included, with maples, oaks, and honey locusts leading the field in numbers.

The chapter on "Trees Make the Town" is most pertinent and valuable, not only for older cities but also for newly developed areas; information is given on setting up a Shade Tree Commission, and examples cited of cities with special tree plantings.

Other facets of the subject covered include summer and fall leaf coloring, Trees for Seashore Planting, Tree Planting and Care, as well as lists of trees by flower color or having decorative fruits or fall color.

The colored illustrations add much to the value of the book by showing the form, habit and often flowers of many of the trees described. It is much to be hoped that Mr. Flemer's book will aid in the knowledge of what kinds of trees should be planted, and that more will continue to be planted each year to improve the appearance of our streets and cities.

B. O. MULLIGAN

INTRODUCTION

For many reasons the need for trees and tree-planting has never been greater than it is today. And — fortunately — interest in all aspects of tree culture is also at an all-time high.

This book is intended to serve that interest. Written with a minimum of technical terminology, it depends wherever possible on handsome color plates which show, far better than descriptive paragraphs, the countless beauties of trees.

It is not primarily a book on tree identification, though anyone who spends a little time studying the illustrations can hardly fail to improve his ability to recognize the various species. Essentially it is a description and evaluation of nearly 200 trees, large and small, used for ornamental planting. The varieties discussed here have been chosen because of their adaptability to the sub-tropical, temperate, and cold sections of the United States and Canada, and because they will thrive selectively in wet, humid, or desert conditions.

A few words about the arrangement of the book may be helpful. The first section deals with the selection of suitable trees for home grounds and for street and community planting. It also covers the fundamentals underlying the proper location of trees for shade and other types of climate control. To make it easier to compare them, the most important of the flowering trees are grouped together in one section, followed by the larger shade and ornamental trees. Additional valuable small trees and outstanding large trees are described in separate sections.

Tree planting and the care of trees over the years are considered in a later section. Here too are descriptions of pruning techniques and the art of growing espaliered trees. These are followed by listings of trees according to their flower colors, foliage colors both in summer and fall, fruiting characteristics and ornamental bark. Finally there are lists of trees for special purposes and locations, including city conditions, the seashore, arid locations, acid soil, and lists for hot, temperate and very cold climates, with brief accounts of the special problems which these areas present.

In earlier days little was known about the adaptability of tree species to the widely divergent climates of North America. Now, however, there is a wealth of information on tree planting on this continent. Anyone writing about trees today must recognize the vast body of accumulated knowledge which has been patiently amassed by plantsmen in the many excellent arboretums, state and government agencies, and commercial nurseries throughout the land. It was only their efforts in finding and introducing new species, selecting and hybridizing new varieties, and testing and evaluating them over the years, that produced for our enjoyment the marvelous range of trees available to the gardening public today.

WILLIAM FLEMER, III
Princeton, New Jersey

8

SHADE AND ORNAMENTAL
TREES
IN COLOR

ENJOY THE ULTIMATE PLEASURES OF TREES THROUGH WISE LANDSCAPE PLANNING. A NATIVE PACIFIC DOGWOOD IS COMPLEMENTED BY PINES, A FLOWERING CHERRY AND LOW GROWING SHRUBS IN THIS WELL DESIGNED LANDSCAPE.

The pleasures of trees

From the beginning of recorded time trees have been the symbols of life and strength and beauty.

Solomon sang of the Cedars of Lebanon and over many centuries the prophets spoke of them again and again.

In the funerary art of ancient Egypt there are tomb inscriptions of potted or container-grown trees being removed from ships of the Nile to be planted in the Pharaohs' gardens. Today in California you can gaze up at sequoias that were growing before Christ was born.

Trees have been an ever-present part of the history of man, and yet, only a few generations ago — because of the need for land or lumber — vast areas of the world were wantonly or wastefully denuded of their native trees.

True, there were always a few people who sought to preserve trees either for their beauty or utility. Usually it was only the wealthy who could plant and nurture trees on their estates or plantations. But in recent years tree culture has become much more common. There are several reasons for this: the recognition of the need for conservation of natural resources; a more general awareness of the practical benefits and beauty of trees; transportation changes which have made it possible for people of relatively modest means to live beyond the confines of urban centers; and increase in the financial and educational status of large segments of the population — all of these in ways that are oblique and sometimes strange have contributed to a remarkable increase in the popular interest in trees.

In brief text and full color pictures, this book is intended to show the world of trees in their infinitely varied beauty of foliage, color and texture, flowers and fruit. The new gardener will find it a survey of the most useful

11

trees in his area and a guide to their selection, planting and care. The experienced gardener will find in these pages a description of many exciting new trees developed by plant breeders — many of them so new that they have not yet found their way into garden literature.

Trees may be separated for convenience into four separate classes. 1. Deciduous trees, those like most of our oaks, maples and cherries for example, which shed their leaves in the fall, are bare throughout the winter, and grow an entire new crop of leaves the following spring. 2. Broadleaf evergreen trees, like the live oak, evergreen magnolia and hollies for example, with broad veined leaves which remain green on the tree throughout the winter, and are only gradually replaced in the following growing season. 3. Coniferous trees, most of which are evergreen and all of which bear narrow, needle-like leaves, such as pines, spruce and firs. 4. Palms which, although evergreen and of tree size, belong to the great division of the plant kingdom which includes the grasses and our garden lilies.

For further convenience, trees may be still more arbitrarily separated by size into two general classes: major or large trees, generally taller than 40 feet at maturity, and minor or small trees, 40 feet or smaller at maturity. The latter include some varieties which often grow like tall shrubs but can be trimmed up into a single-trunked form.

DECIDIOUS FOLIAGE OF (1) SWEETGUM AND (2) PIN OAK

EVERGREEN FOLIAGE OF AMERICAN HOLLY

NEEDLE-LIKE LEAVES OF A CONIFEROUS EVERGREEN DEODAR CEDAR

EVERGREEN FAN SHAPED FOLIAGE OF A MEDITERRANIAN PALM TREE

How to select trees for the home grounds

In selecting trees for the home grounds you must think first of the climate of the area. The varieties chosen must be those which thrive in that particular zone. Obviously southern types like evergreen magnolias or palms will not survive in the north central states, and trees of northern origin such as the sugar maple will not thrive in Florida and southern Texas. In the descriptions which follow, the trees are indicated as being hardy in a given zone, their northern limit of reliable hardiness. These zones, which were carefully worked out by horticulturists, are shown on the map of Canada and the United States which ap-

pears below. On a map of this scale they cannot be minutely accurate and there are local variations due to altitude, proximity to large bodies of water, and soil type which modify hardiness.

The second consideration is the size of the home grounds and the amount of space available. If you live on a small lot, you will have room for only a small tree of limited size at maturity. Where space is more generous, large growing trees may be planted along with several smaller trees to give a variety of blooming seasons, fruiting effects and interesting forms. In general, trees should be planted which at

Continued on page 17

HARDINESS ZONES OF THE UNITED STATES AND CANADA
Prepared by The Arnold Arboretum

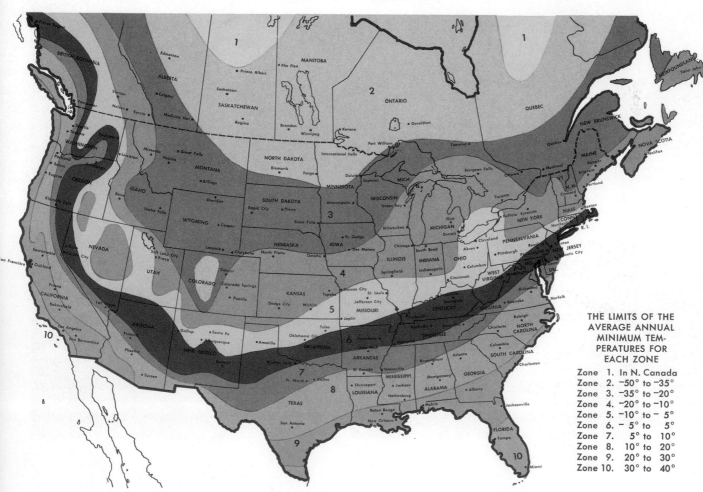

THE LIMITS OF THE
AVERAGE ANNUAL
MINIMUM TEM-
PERATURES FOR
EACH ZONE

Zone 1. In N. Canada
Zone 2. −50° to −35°
Zone 3. −35° to −20°
Zone 4. −20° to −10°
Zone 5. −10° to − 5°
Zone 6. − 5° to   5°
Zone 7.   5° to 10°
Zone 8. 10° to 20°
Zone 9. 20° to 30°
Zone 10. 30° to 40°

A LABURNUM, DRAPED IN CHAINS OF GOLDEN BLOOM, CREATES A DELIGHTFUL ACCENT IN THIS LANDSCAPE. Laburnum vossi. See page 78

14

CRIMSON EUCALYPTUS, Eucalyptus ficifolia. See page 93

CHINESE PISTACHE, Pistacia chinensis. See page 80

TULIP TREE, Liriodendron tulipifera. See page 89

RED OAK, Quercus borealis. See page 69

15

THE SPACIOUS GROUNDS OF THIS ESTATE ARE A PERFECT SETTING FOR THE AMERICAN ELM.
Ulmus americana. See page 73

maturity are in some relation to the scale of the house. A small house may appear still more dwarfed if surrounded by very tall trees and a large house is especially handsome when set off by majestic specimens, although there are exceptions to this general rule. Everyone has seen country cottages in tasteful proximity to towering mature trees, but such combinations are most happy in rural areas where the size of the tree is in harmony with the much larger open space around it.

A further consideration is the character of the tree itself. The number of species which will thrive in city gardens is much more limited than those available for suburban planting be-cause of the polluted atmosphere, poor soil, and limited water penetration. Trees for sea-shore homes must be selected from those va-rieties which will withstand salt-laden winds and coastal soil. Poplars and willows are poor choices for shade tree planting because their roots actively search for water and will invade and clog sewer lines. Deep rooted species are less competitive with lawns and flower beds than those with shallow wide-spreading root systems. Species with large broad leaves re-quire more leaf disposal than those with tiny leaflets like Honeylocusts which sift incon-spicuously into lawns and shrub beds.

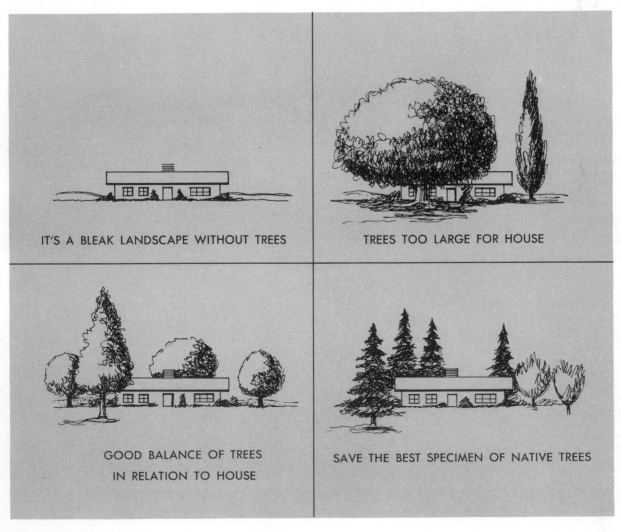

IT'S A BLEAK LANDSCAPE WITHOUT TREES

TREES TOO LARGE FOR HOUSE

GOOD BALANCE OF TREES
IN RELATION TO HOUSE

SAVE THE BEST SPECIMEN OF NATIVE TREES

17

THIS SHADEMASTER LOCUST (Plant Patent 1515) CASTS LIGHT-DAPPLED SHADE THAT PERMITS GOOD LAWN GROWTH. See page 66

18

Trees in the landscape

Trees are the dominant features of the landscape and should be so treated. They can be planted to serve a number of important functions. One of the most important is climate control. There is an enormous difference between a new suburban development on open land, exposed to the full blast of sun and wind, and the same area a decade later when the newly planted trees have developed enough to cast welcome pools of cool shade. Properly sited trees can break the force of prevailing cold winds and create a more temperate local climate. Experience with shelter-belt planting on the western plains has demonstrated repeatedly the great moderating affect of trees on the microclimate.

Street trees are planted both for shade and for colorful effects of flowers and autumn foliage. A driver feels an immediate sense of relief on a hot summer day when entering a shady street of mature trees because their cool shade reduces the temperature of the street, and the eyestrain from the glaring sunlight is eliminated. Streets planted with the smaller flowering trees are often the most beautiful sections of the entire community. Experiments in urban renewal have shown that streets in decaying areas which are face-lifted by planting with showy flowering trees experience a reversal of the decline, and property values increase as the newly inspired owners begin to improve their homes and yards.

WELCOME POOLS OF SHADE

AN INVITING AVENUE OF SHADE

A LINDEN TREE CREATES DENSE SHADE FOR COMFORTABLE OUTDOOR LIVING IN THE SUMMER MONTHS. See page 71

TREES CREATE SOUND AND WIND BARRIERS TO PROVIDE GREATER COMFORT AND PRIVACY IN OUTDOOR LIVING AREAS.

FLOWERING HAWTHORNS DECORATE THIS STREET WITH COLORFUL DISPLAYS OF FLOWERS IN SPRING. THEIR RED FRUIT ATTRACT AND FEED BIRDS IN FALL AND WINTER MONTHS. See page 37

Trees around the home

Trees planted on home grounds serve many functions. Properly sited, they frame the front of the house and give it a handsome setting. They create permanent low-maintenance shaded areas in the yard for comfortable outdoor living in the summer months. Planted at the rear of the property, they create a beautiful background for the garden, often with spectacular floral or fruiting displays in season. They are the best materials for screening out unwanted views or ugly structures which would otherwise detract from the beauty of the yard.

Where space is adequate, avenues of shade or flowering trees can be planted to create vistas and draw the eye to distant landscape features such as a view of water or mountains. Flowering tree specimens in the yard are as beautiful in their season as are large flower beds and they require far less maintenance. The presence of trees is necessary to attract many species of birds, and a planting of those species with fruits important to bird life will greatly increase the number of birds which can be seen and enjoyed at close range in the home garden.

A CUTLEAF RED MAPLE LENDS CHARM AND COLOR TO THIS WELL-DESIGNED LANDSCAPE.

How to place trees

The shade of a tree falling on a house greatly lowers its temperature during the hot summer months. The value of this effect has not been diminished by the increase in electrical air conditioning in recent years. The same shade which cools a house not air conditioned will also greatly reduce the cost of operating an air conditioner during the expensive summer months. Trees are nature's original air conditioner and operate both by intercepting and absorbing the hot sun rays and also by the cooling effect of water constantly evaporating from the acres of leaf surface which each mature shade tree possesses. A deciduous tree planted on the southwest side of a house will cool it during the summer when shade is necessary but not in winter when the leaves have fallen and the sun's heat is desired.

In areas where wind protection is important, the direction of prevailing winds should be considered in locating trees. If hot summer winds are normal from the west, a group of trees located to the west of the property will temper the wind flow and cool the air that passes through their branches. If cold winter winds regularly sweep down from the north west, a screen planting of evergreen trees on that side of the property will markedly reduce winter heating bills as well as greatly prolong the season when the garden may be enjoyed outdoors.

Except for espaliered trees actually trained on the walls themselves, trees should not be planted very close to the house. Large growing trees should be planted at least 30 feet away, and small types at least 15 feet away from the foundation. Low spreading types, like some of the flowering crabapples for example, should not be planted closer than 15 feet away from driveways or walks unless it is planned to trim them up very high to give vehicular or pedestrian clearance. Deciduous shade and flowering trees should be planted to cast shade on a patio or terrace if it is located in full sunlight. Such a tree properly located will greatly increase the utility of the patio area during the summer months and be far more beautiful and permanent than any cloth umbrella or sun shade. Trees for patio planting should not be large fruiting varieties or those which drop leaves over a long period in the late summer and fall, as these will require removal.

In street tree planting a common tendency is to plant large growing varieties like oaks and maples entirely too closely for proper spacing at maturity. Sixty feet apart is a minimum spacing for most large trees and 80 feet is better. To avoid a long period of barren "underplanted" appearance on a new street while the trees are young, an excellent plan is to interplant the large growing varieties with smaller growing species like flowering trees. These give an immediate effect, years of beauty, and are generally beginning to decline just when the larger slower maturing specimens are coming into their prime. The one absolute and invariable rule is NEVER to plant an entire town or community with one single species or variety of tree, no matter how desirable it may then seem to be. Experiences with the Dutch elm disease have shown what costly and heartbreaking tragedies result from breaking this rule.

ASH TREE SITUATED TO PROTECT THE HOUSE FROM THE HOT AFTERNOON SUN.

23

The row of Poplars above provides protection to the house from hot summer winds. Poplars are well chosen here due to their rapid growth and narrow columnar growth habit. Due to susceptibility to disease they may not survive to maturity thus it is wise to make a secondary planting of other more lasting, though slower growing, trees. Note the planting of smaller trees above that will provide permanent protection after the poplars are removed.

The clumps of birch at left will provide protection from winds and reduce street noise while providing shade for outdoor living during warm summer days. Their striking trunk marking add interest and beauty during the winter months.

This street planting of Red Maples illustrates correct spacing of trees that will eventually attain great size. Sixty to eighty feet spacing is necessary to allow natural healthy growth of the large trees. Choose with care the trees you plant. Where no overhead wires are used these Red Maples will be well suited to this street side location. Lower growing varieties would be better suited to similar situations if power and telephone wires were overhead.

This Tea Crab Apple has been given a choice location in the landscape pictured below. It is located where it can be seen and admired from the house. Plant large trees at least 30 feet and small trees 15 feet from buildings. Prune lower branches of lawn trees to allow easy maintenance of grass.

How to preserve existing trees

An effort should be made to preserve desirable specimens of trees thriving on a selected building site. They become even more valuable when used as the foundation for further landscaping. Work them into your landscape plan and insure their preservation for years of enjoyment.

Not all new homes are built on plots of completely open land, and in many instances there are already large existing trees on the home lot. These trees are often desirable specimens of completely hardy local species. The great problem with the wooded home lot is to get the builder to leave the trees undamaged rather than mutilate them with excavating and grading equipment. After construction has been completed the trees can be surveyed, the best specimens saved, and undesirable types carefully removed or thinned out. Often it is best to create a woodland or shade garden in such a yard. It is a rewarding form of gardening and easier than trying to create a large lawn and struggling to grow sun loving shrubs and flowers.

The most destructive thing that can happen to trees is a change in the soil level in which they are growing. If the grade must be radically altered to build the house, especially in areas with an impervious clay soil, the best solution is to remove all the trees in the altered area. This drastic treatment is often far better than to struggle along with declining trees which will ultimately die anyhow, and be an eyesore while they are in the process.

The value of this great beech tree was realized by the builder and necessary precautions have been taken to protect it during construction work.

The ancient apple tree at right once grew as one of many fruiting trees in an orchard. Its great character and beauty was appreciated by those who would live under its gnarled branches and now adds charm and comfort for all who relax in this intimate patio.

TREE FORMS

ROUNDED

OVAL

PYRAMIDAL

COLUMNAR

FASTIGATE

WEEPING

ARCHING

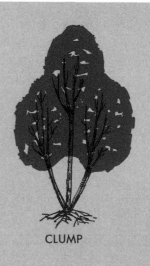

CLUMP

Modern trends in tree selection

In former times tree varieties were frequently planted solely because they were easy to transplant and rapid in growth. Such species as Carolina Poplars, Silver Maples and Siberian Elms which seemed to be entirely satisfactory in their vigorous youth developed into brittle unsightly mature trees unsuitable for home planting and costly to remove. They are rarely planted today.

Even among desirable shade tree species, trees of seedling origin and unpredictable performance were commonly planted in the past. The present trend is to select wherever possible the occasional vastly superior specimen trees which appear, and propagate them vegetatively by grafting on seedling rootstocks and use these first class varieties of known and predictable future growth for shade tree planting. Both commercial nursery and governmental tree breeders are at work creating superior trees and hybrids and these too are being vegetatively propagated for planting. The cost of such improved trees is only a little greater than that of seedling grown trees, and in the long run they are actually much cheaper because of greatly reduced spraying or pruning costs in future years. No fruit grower today would dream of planting an orchard of seedling fruit trees. The same principle is being extended to shade and ornamental tree planting.

Sources of information

In addition to the excellent books on tree selection and care, there are many other sources of information. Of especial value and interest are the famous arboretums throughout the country such as the Arnold Arboretum in Boston, The Morton Arboretum in Lisle, Illinois, the National Arboretum in Washington, and many others. Here are assembled large collections of young and mature trees of every kind, properly labeled; here also are staffs of expert horticulturists. State Universities, botanic gardens, and private estates are also valuable sources of demonstration plantings and information. Most State Universities and the U.S. Department of Agriculture publish informational bulletins and books. Local and mail order nurseries distribute catalogues and concise and accurate information on trees and their planting and care. Reliable firms with jealously guarded reputations and often generations of dependable service are in no way to be confused with the flashy "one shot" promotions of unscrupulous fly-by-night firms which advertise a "miracle tree" with grossly exaggerated claims and then evaporate after fleecing the gullible public. As in every other line of commercial endeavor, cheap shoddy merchandise is a poor buy. An investment in quality trees supplied by a reliable nursery will give a lifetime of enjoyment and beauty.

Trees make the town

Everybody recognizes subconsciously that well grown trees improve the community in which they are located. Quite aside from the quality of the homes involved, the choicest residential area of a community is recognized by the spacious well-kept grounds surrounding each house. In these handsomely landscaped areas the trees play a dominant role in setting the dignity and beauty of the whole picture. Today there is a much clearer realization of the very real and exact dollar value inherent in a community shade tree. Even the somewhat jaundiced eye of the Bureau of Internal Revenue recognizes the monetary value of trees by permitting tax deductions for their loss on exactly the same basis as deductions are allowed for the involuntary destruction of a building or any other tangible physical property. The value of a tree varies of course with the species of tree and the geographical location of the community in which it is growing, and generalizations are very difficult to arrive at. Nevertheless a recent study undertaken by an arborists' organization indicated that shade trees established and growing on a community street had an average value of $50.00 per inch of diameter (measured at breast height). It is not the purpose of this discussion to limit the importance of trees to their cold cash value alone, but rather to indicate that when private home owners or civic or municipal organizations plant trees, they are making an investment which steadily grows in value during the long life of the trees themselves.

Not only our own country but most of the densely populated countries the world over are coming to grips with the long-ignored but now unavoidable problems of urban renewal. The major dilemma facing all too many large cities today is the pernicious decay of the heart of the city, overbuilt, congested and ugly. Drastic surgery is often the only remedy. Old buildings are torn down, new ones are built which utilize less ground space, and small park areas with trees and ground covers are introduced to woo back the pedestrian. Trees are one of the important tools for successful urban renewal and are a part of almost every project.

Residential areas are subject to the same vicissitudes as down-town business areas. They may have character and distinction almost permanently, or they may decline at an accelerated rate with crippling losses in property values and tax yields. The experiments which Edward H. Scanlon made when he was Shade Tree Commissioner in Cleveland, Ohio, clearly demonstrated that replanting a deteriorating area with new and superior trees was an effective way to reverse this decline. His findings have been confirmed many times by experiences in other towns and cities. Just as in the renewal of city business districts, trees are an integral part of an attack on residential area degeneration.

COLUMNAR MAPLES RELIEVE THE HORIZONTAL ARCHITECTURAL LINES IN THIS INDUSTRIAL LANDSCAPE. See page 60

Most of the battle to preserve property values is won in advance, of course, if new communities are properly planned before they are ever built. "Garden Cities" or "New Towns" are not new to this country and their history has been largely a happy one, with stable or increasing property values over long periods. They are even older and more abundant in England, and many with a half century of existence are still as desirable places in which to live as they were when first laid out. Well planned community design, safe attractive recreational parks and play areas, and inviting tree-shaded streets continue to attract and hold desirable residents just as they did in the beginning. Major portions of our country are running out of land at an alarming and geometrically increasing rate. Unplanned urban sprawl is a doubtful luxury we can no longer afford. It is every citizen's duty to see that the new housing of the present and future is properly planned and properly planted, or our descendants will remember with sorrow and chagrin that we lived in the last "golden age" and took no thought for them.

Most communities which have recognized the importance of shade trees in creating and maintaining better living have found it wise to establish Shade Tree Commissions. A Commission is a municipal body, an arm of municipal government, which controls and regulates shade tree planting and maintainance on the community streets. Its advantages are manifold, most important being the continuity and order it enforces. The commissioners normally serve without pay, and in staggered terms so that, as a group, they become thoroughly cognizant of shade tree problems and practice. There is often a full-time paid tree warden with a trained staff of men who plant, fertilize, water and trim trees on a year-round basis. This man and his staff are salaried municipal employees. Smaller towns who do not feel ready for a large staff, often have only a salaried tree warden or paid consulting arborist who keeps watch on the trees and their condition. When contracts are let for planting or maintenance, they are under his experienced supervision and enforcement. The Commission decides on what are the best tree species and varieties for street tree use in their particular area and publishes a list of approved trees which can be planted on city streets. This prevents unscrupulous developers from planting unsuitable but cheap trees on city streets merely to fulfill F.H.A. requirements.

A Shade Tree Commission is organized by enacting a municipal ordinance establishing it and defining its duties. A shade tree ordinance should cover the following points:

The appointment and replacement of Commission personnel.

Salaries of officers and employes.

The powers of the Commission.

How trees and improvements are to be paid for.

How hearings will be held covering proposed plantings and removals.

Penalties for violations of Commission ordinances.

THIS WOODED PARK WILL REWARD NEARBY RESIDENTS WITH ECONOMIC AND SOCIAL BENEFITS.

TREES MAKE THE TOWN—Continued

Authority to promulgate additional ordinances.

How public notice of regulations is to be filed.

Limitations of liability of the Commission and its individual members.

A complete and thoroughly tested model ordinance is published by the New Jersey Federation of Shade Tree Commissions which has its permanent headquarters at the Rutgers University College of Agriculture in New Brunswick, New Jersey. Copies may be secured by writing its Executive Secretary.

In enacting an ordinance the municipality, or the county, as is more often the case in rural districts, assumes responsibility for the shade trees growing on municipal street property or in parks. Thereafter it has complete control of tree planting, maintenance, and removal in these areas. In many cases it will buy and plant trees of approved varieties on home owner's front yard property if the home owners agree to easements permitting the municipality to retain control of the trees. Where the Commission purchases trees for home owners, the

FAMILIES ON THIS STREET COOPERATED IN SELECTING AND PLANTING KWANZAN CHERRIES. See pages 48-49

price is lower than what an individual would pay because all individual orders are combined and a large aggregate quantity is taken at once.

Garden clubs, service clubs, and other civic groups often take on special tree planting projects for community improvement. Such projects may include planting collections of beautiful flowering trees in parks, malls, or other municipally controlled areas, planting school grounds, establishing arboretums for educational purposes and for beauty, and planting living memorials to commemorate war casualties or prominent citizens. Several communities have greatly enriched their shade tree resources by encouraging citizens to commemorate loved ones by planting trees in their memory. The name of the person remembered is displayed on a tasteful bronze marker set flush on the ground near the tree. Many a community owes the existence of its Shade Tree Commission to an active civic group which sponsored the move and aroused the public support to make it possible.

A popular garden or service club project is to associate the town with a special kind or group of flowering trees. Thus several towns in Virginia have made extensive plantings of flowering dogwoods, others in Maryland have planted many flowering cherries and now rival Washington in the spring time. Some towns in New Jersey and in Iowa have established mass plantings of ornamental crab apples which are of breathtaking beauty in the blooming season. Millville, New Jersey has designated itself as the Holly City, and has started extensive American Holly plantings which will be of outstanding beauty for generations to come. These communities plant many other species as shade trees, but their own special ornamental plantings set them above the general run of towns and make them unusually interesting and beautiful places in which to live. We need many more such imaginative projects to combat the sameness and standardization which is an unfortunate feature of American and Canadian suburbia.

Flowering trees
THE DOGWOODS

No group of flowering trees has greater year round beauty than the dogwoods. Visitors from Europe never cease to marvel at the breath-taking spring display of our eastern Flowering Dogwood. The indispensable but less well known Japanese Dogwood is of equal merit, and the magnificent Pacific Dogwood stands alone as the finest of all the native west coast flowering trees. The dogwoods are not as widely adaptable as the flowering crab apples and re-quire a mildly acid, fertile soil and reasonable moisture to succeed. These conditions preclude their use in a large part of the arid and the central midwest and they are not reliably hardy in northern New England and most of Canada. Wherever they can be grown, they combine the best qualities sought in flowering trees, spectacular floral display, interesting branching patterns, rich autumn foliage colors, and highly ornamental fruits.

PINK AND WHITE FLOWERING DOGWOODS, Cornus florida and C. f. rubra

PINK FLOWERING DOGWOOD, Cornus florida rubra

FLOWERING DOGWOOD
Cornus florida

Everybody who lives in the area where this splendid plant can be grown is familiar with its lavish display of large 4 petaled (bracted) flowers, borne on flat horizontal branches. Less appreciated but equally colorful are the rich wine reds and scarlets of the fall foliage and the clusters of glossy red fruits. The normal wild dogwoods have pure white flowers, but delicate pink specimens are not uncommon.

Of the many pink forms, one with especially rich color was early discovered, propagated, and named the Red Flowering Dogwood — *Cornus florida rubra*. Its color varies somewhat depending on the soil in which it is grown and

the age of the flowers, but newly opened flowers are often a clear full red, most admired when it is planted in combination with white flowering specimens. There is also a double white flowered form of dogwood which stays in full bloom far longer than the normal type, but the classic dogwood flower shape is lost, and of course it does not fruit in the fall.

The Florida Dogwood is native from southern Massachusetts to Florida and like any tree with so great a native range it varies considerably in hardiness. It must be stated that only the plants originating from northern sources are hardy in Zone 4, the red form is hardy only in Zone 5 and the more southerly strains are more tender still.

34

JAPANESE DOGWOOD, Cornus kousa

PACIFIC DOGWOOD, Cornus nuttalli

JAPANESE DOGWOOD
Cornus kousa

This Oriental Dogwood is just as colorful and useful as our native plant. The flowers have 4 sharply pointed petals (bracts) rather than notched ones as in the Florida Dogwood and this gives a star effect to the blooms. Most important, it comes into bloom a month later than the native variety and hence gives a whole second season of dogwood bloom. Also, coming into flower in warmer, more settled weather, it is never nipped by late frosts and has a very long period of bloom. Mature specimens have the same graceful horizontal branches as the Flowering Dogwood and the fall color is a glowing brocade of crimson and scarlet. The fruits are globular, like red raspberries and stand out on long stems, being effective in late summer. The fruits of both species are first rate bird foods. The Japanese Dogwood is hardy in Zone 5 and requires a mildly acid soil and good soil moisture to grow well.

PACIFIC DOGWOOD
Cornus nuttalli

A magnificent flowering tree growing into a much larger specimen than other dogwoods, the Pacific Dogwood thrives only in the cool humid climate of the Pacific northwest in Zone 7 from California to British Columbia. The flowers normally have 6 petals (bracts) rather than 4 and open in April, with sometimes a second scattered bloom in early September. The bright red berries color up in late summer and the orange scarlet fall foliage is noteworthy. Curiously enough, this variety grows well in Great Britain and in parts of Europe where the eastern Flowering Dogwood barely exists. While the Pacific Dogwood is not worth trying in the east or midwest, it is a first rate flowering tree for gardens within its native west coast range.

35

PAUL'S SCARLET HAWTHORN, Crataegus oxyacantha pauli—See Page 38

THE HAWTHORNS

The hawthorns form an interesting group of small spreading trees frequently planted for their abundant flowers, handsome foliage, and colorful long lasting fruit. They are members of the enormous rose family, and are somewhat closely allied to the wild crab apples. Practically all of the hawthorns are very thorny, some species with long recurving spines up to 3 inches in length. As a group, they are exceedingly tough and hardy, thriving in a very wide range of soil types and even under harsh city conditions where atmospheric pollution and starved dry soil will speedily kill most other flowering trees. The fruits of many varieties are very long lasting and retain their brilliant color late into the winter. Their flowers are mostly white, rarely pink or red, and are borne at an important period in late spring long after cherries, crab apples and other traditional spring flowering trees have ceased blooming. Hawthorns have been used since time immemorial as hedges in England and Europe to screen and protect gardens and as living fences to confine livestock in fields and pastures. This is because they respond well to the hedging shears and are easily clipped to form impenetrable barriers. Thus they are excellent dual purpose plants either trimmed up in tree form with natural spreading heads, or clipped to make medium or tall hedges which will turn away the most determined trespasser.

DOWNY HAWTHORN
Crataegus mollis

This is one of the largest growing of the hawthorns and is well adapted to trimming up into standard or tree form. The horizontal branching of mature specimens and the ample clusters of white flowers (unusually large for a hawthorn, one inch across) make it a good substitute for Flowering Dogwood in the extensive central sections of this country and Canada where the Flowering Dogwoods cannot be grown. The fruits also are unusually large and make a splendid show when they turn red in late summer.

It is fully hardy in Zone 4 and can be grown in a wide range of soil types.

TOBA HAWTHORN
Crataegus mordenensis 'Toba'

Toba is a new very hardy hybrid hawthorn (Zone 3) which originated in Manitoba, Canada, a cross between Paul's Scarlet Hawthorn and the very hardy native Fleshy Hawthorn, *Crataegus succulenta*. It most successfully combines the best qualities of both parents, the plant hybridist's dream come true. From the native parent it inherits great hardiness and thick leathery foliage which is unaffected by the leaf spot fungi which plague European species in much of this country. From Paul's Scarlet it inherits the large double flowers of a fine rose pink color which are conspicuous for a long flowering period. The Toba Hawthorn is destined for wide planting in the areas where the English Hawthorns do not thrive.

DOWNY HAWTHORN, Crataegus mollis

ENGLISH HAWTHORN
Crataegus oxyacantha

This beautiful and quite variable species has been cultivated and admired for centuries, and a number of varieties have been developed and perpetuated. It grows into a small round-headed tree with dense branches and short thorns less than 1 inch in length. The leaves are small and deeply lobed. While the English Hawthorn is hardy in Zone 4 it grows best in the temperate areas along the coasts of the northeast and northwest and is at its finest in the cool-summer areas of northern California and Oregon.

Of the many horticultural varieties named and propagated, the two most outstanding are the following.

PAUL'S SCARLET HAWTHORN
Crataegus oxyacantha pauli

This variety is unique in its family for its fully double bright red flowers which, being sterile, are retained on the plant for a long period. It is always grown in tree form and makes an exceedingly handsome specimen when in full bloom in late spring. It bears only a very few inconspicuous fruits.

DOUBLE WHITE HAWTHORN
Crataegus oxyacantha plena

This handsome companion plant to the above bears large clusters of pure glistening white, fully double flowers like miniature pompoms. It fruits somewhat more abundantly than Paul's Scarlet Hawthorn but is planted for its long lasting flowers rather than as a fruiting tree.

WASHINGTON HAWTHORN
Crataegus phaenopyrum

This is one of the best of the many native North American species for garden planting. It can be grown as a multiple stemmed clump, branched low, or trimmed up readily into

WASHINGTON HAWTHORN
Crataegus phaenopyrum

AS THIS WINTER-TIME PHOTOGRAPH SHOWS, THE WASHINGTON HAWTHORN BEARS AN UN-EQUALED DISPLAY OF LONG-LASTING ORANGE-RED FRUITS.

standard or tree form. It bears masses of white flowers late in the spring which give rise to clusters of bright orange red fruits. The fruits are very hard and last unblemished through the hard freezes of winter into the early spring. The glossy three lobed leaves are handsome all summer and spectacular in the fall when they turn brilliant shades of orange and scarlet. Hardy in Zone 4 and adaptable to all sorts of soils and conditions, the Washington Hawthorn is second to none for street, park or garden planting.

38

SOUTHERN MAGNOLIA, Magnolia grandiflora

THE MAGNOLIAS

The Orient and the east coast of the United States are the two areas of origin for the magnolia family, botanically a very ancient and primitive group which includes some of our most spectacular flowering trees. The varieties which grow easily in our country range from the very dwarf, almost shrubby Star Magnolia from Japan to the magnificent evergreen Southern Magnolia, native from the Carolinas to Texas, which reaches 100 feet in height. With their bold tropical-appearing foliage and enormous fragrant flowers, they bring a lush exotic effect to any home or community planting.

The magnolias grow to perfection in rich acid soil with adequate moisture and will not survive in strongly alkaline soil or the continental climate of the north central U.S.A. and Canada. Curiously enough, however, some do not object to city soot and gases and some fine Southern Magnolias can be found in downtown Washington, D.C. and Saucer Magnolias in New York City. The whole group has thick rather fleshy roots which do not heal and regenerate quickly after injury. For this reason best success is obtained by transplanting magnolias with a ball of earth or planting specimens grown in containers, and by planting them in early spring. These spring-moved plants start out into growth at once and much more readily establish themselves in the new location than fall or winter-moved trees which are in the process of going dormant.

The Magnolia Family is a big one with many trees of great horticultural merit, many more than can be described within the confines of this book. Those interested in further exploration are urged to join the newly formed American Magnolia Society, an active group of amateurs and professionals interested in growing and developing this beautiful family of trees.

YULAN MAGNOLIA
Magnolia denudata (M. conspicua)

This slow growing Chinese variety with its large 6 inch flowers of purest white will ultimately make a tree up to 40 feet in height. When crossed with the low growing purple *Magnolia liliflora,* it gave rise to the indispensable pink Saucer Magnolia and its many colorful sister hybrids. The Yulan is hardy in Zone 5 and makes a fine neat medium-sized tree with clean pest-free foliage and an unsurpassed crop of dazzling white flowers each spring. It blends with any color or texture of house surface, and when underplanted with beds of dwarf scillas, crocus or other early spring bulbs, forms a picture never to be forgotten.

SOUTHERN MAGNOLIA OR BULL BAY
Magnolia grandiflora

Here is one of the most beautiful large flowering trees in the world, including the most spectacular tropical forms. In the low rich swamp lands of its native territory from the Carolinas south through Florida to Texas it makes an impressive tree at maturity up to 100 feet in height and 50 or more feet in width. It can be grown considerably north of its native range and thrives throughout Zone 7 on both the east and west coasts. This magnolia is fully evergreen, with glossy broad dark green leaves 6 to 9 inches in length, making splendid cut greens in winter for house decoration. The huge waxy white flowers like fragrant ivory cups are borne over a very long period from May on into the summer rather than briefly in the spring like so many of the oriental magnolias. For foliage and flowers, the Southern Magnolia has no equal among the evergreen trees which can be grown in this country.

SAUCER MAGNOLIA
Magnolia soulangeana

This vigorous hybrid variety of French origin is the most frequently planted garden variety up through Zone 5 and especially wherever the Southern Magnolia is not hardy. The pink form is the hardiest of the many varieties arising from this cross between the Yulan and the purple *Magnolia liliflora*. It develops normally into a large clump of stems reaching an ultimate height of 30 feet and covered each spring with large tulip-shaped flowers, pink on the outside of the petals and white inside, opening to 6 to 10 inches in width. About a week later in flower and equally beautiful is the variety Alexandrina with big 7 inch cup-shaped flowers a rich deep rosy purple on the outside and white on the inside of the petals. The darkest variety of all is Lennei which is an even darker purple on the outside of the petals and blooms late enough to escape damage from the occasional late spring frosts. The Saucer Magnolias do surprisingly well in the city and the contrast between their startling display of tropical appearing flowers and their smooth pale grey bark enlivens many a drab city park.

LENNE MAGNOLIA, Magnolia soulangeana 'Lennei'

THE LAST TO BLOOM OF ALL THE SOULANGEANA HYBRIDS, THE LENNEI MAGNOLIA, ESCAPES DAMAGE FROM LATE SPRING FROSTS.

HITE SAUCER MAGNOLIA, Magnolia soulangeana 'Alba'

SAUCER MAGNOLIA, Magnolia soulangeana

STAR MAGNOLIA
Magnolia stellata

This is one of the slowest growing and dwarf forms of the MAGNOLIAS with narrow 2 to 4 inch leaves and bearing thousands of pure white or pale pink intensely fragrant double flowers early in the spring. The tree is hardy in Zone 5, even hardier than the Saucer Magnolia, but blooms so early that the flowers are sometimes damaged by spring frosts. If planted in a cold north-facing location the blooming is delayed and it often escapes the flower damage that occurs on plants in a warm sheltered location which are forced into early bloom. Being a dwarf slow developing form which rarely reaches 20 feet in height in extreme old age, the Star Magnolia and its pink form *Magnolia stellata rosea* are most useful for small gardens which do not have sufficient room for the larger magnolias.

SWEET BAY
Magnolia virginiana (M. glauca)

Although less spectacular than the oriental magnolias, the Sweet Bay has a subtle beauty which appeals to the sophisticated gardener. This shrubby native magnolia is deserving of a prominent place in the garden in Zone 5. It makes a sizeable narrow evergreen tree in the southern part of its range but is deciduous and shrubby up to 20 feet in height in the northern end of its range in Massachusetts. The leaves are a fine jade green above and white beneath, forming a colorful contrast. The white cup-shaped flowers 2 to 3 inches across are borne successively over a long period in late spring and have a rich pervading fragrance. It is a swamp plant in the wild but will thrive in any good acid garden soil just as well. It produces fruit pods much like cucumbers that split open to reveal the red seeds in the fall.

STAR MAGNOLIA, Magnolia stellata

THE FLOWERING CRAB APPLES

Of all the different kinds of flowering trees, there is no group which is useful over a greater part of this country than the flowering crab apples. Except for the sub-tropical regions of Zones 9 and 10 in the warmest part of Florida and California, they can be successfully grown in all of the states, and the exceptionally hardy Siberian Crab and its hybrids can be grown far north into Canada as well. The flowering crabs are the wild apples collected from all over the north temperate zone of the globe and the innumerable hybrids and crosses between them which have arisen either by chance or design during the long period they have been grown and admired. From one of them *(Malus pumila)* our fruiting varieties of apples were derived.

There are many good reasons for the enormous popularity of the flowering crabs. Their greatest beauty is displayed in the spring when they are covered with fragrant flowers, mostly single and some double flowering, in a wide range of colors from rosy reds through various shades of pink to the pure glistening whites of some varieties. Their habit of branching is varied and interesting too. Some few are narrow and upright, many are dense and bushy, while others have picturesque twisted and con-

toured branches, and a few are of graceful weeping habit. As fall approaches, many crab-apples have a second or bonus season of great beauty, when the tiny apples turn rich shades of yellow and red often enhanced by a brilliant glossy surface or a delicate waxy "bloom". Some varieties ripen and drop their fruits early in the fall, but others retain them very late into winter after all the leaves have fallen. These latter kinds, especially the ones with the smaller fruits, are of great value as fall bird food, and planting them will attract many birds to the home grounds.

There are literally hundreds of varieties of ornamental crabs suitable for home planting. Many of them are quite similar with only minor differences in flower or fruiting habit. The following varieties are selected because each is outstanding in its class or color. They are by no means the only ones well worth planting, but anybody choosing some trees for home or community beautification would be well advised to consider these varieties first. Gardeners interested in learning more about this interesting group should read the excellent book *Ornamental Crab Apples* by Arie F. den Boer and published by The American Association of Nurserymen.

HOPA FLOWERING CRAB APPLES

ALMEY CRAB APPLE
Malus 'Almey'

One of the newer vigorous red flowering hybrid crab apples widely planted for its abundant clear rosy red flowers each with a white star in its center. It forms a wide rounded head and is of rapid growth. It is a Canadian hybrid of the very hardy Siberian Crab and hence is well adapted to the harsh climate of the northern central states in Zone 3. The tree blooms when very young, grows rapidly to an ultimate height of 35 feet and bears quantities of early ripening orange to red fruits up to one inch in diameter. The leaves are an attractive purple color when young and bronze green when mature.

ARNOLD CRAB APPLE
Malus arnoldiana

This shapely hybrid crab originated in the famous Arnold Arboretum near Boston, Massachusetts and is popular because of its profuse blooming. The long slender flower buds are deep red when they appear, become pink and finally white when fully open. Since the flowers open gradually, a colorful contrast is created between the red buds and white open flowers appearing simultaneously in the same cluster. The Arnold Crab forms a dense regular head, ultimately 20 feet in height, and is well adapted to the small garden. It is hardy in Zone 4.

CARMINE CRAB APPLE
Malus atrosanguinea

This splendid hybrid variety from Japan forms a mounded wide spreading crown with interesting twisted branches when mature. It is blanketed with intense carmine red flowers which pale to rosy pink before they drop. No crab apple has finer foliage than the crisp glossy dark green leaves of this variety. The tiny dark red fruits are not particularly noticeable. It is hardy in Zone 4 and of great merit for gardens where limited space is a factor.

The picturesque, contorted branching of a mature specimen fits perfectly in the Japanese Gardens which are becoming so popular in this country today.

SIBERIAN CRAB APPLE
Malus baccata

Here is one of the earliest blooming and hardiest of all the crabs, growing well in Zone 2 far into the interior of Canada. It forms a big upright tree up to 50 feet at maturity and is especially adapted for street tree planting because it can be easily worked up to a 7 or 8 feet clear stem for traffic clearance. The intensely fragrant flowers are pink in bud but a clear white when fully open. The fruits vary among different individual trees but are usually small ($\frac{3}{8}$ inches in diameter) and red or yellow in color. They form an important fall bird food.

SARGENT CRAB APPLE, Malus sargenti

CARMINE CRAB APPLE, Malus atrosanguinea

JAPANESE FLOWERING CRAB APPLE, Malus floribunda

JAPANESE FLOWERING CRAB APPLE
Malus floribunda

The Japanese Crab Apple is a variety with so many merits that it is a standard by which other varieties may be judged. Hardy in Zone 4, it blooms as a very young tree, grows vigorously and forms a wide spreading flat-topped specimen at maturity with a twisted picturesque framework of branches. Like the Arnold Crab, the flowers are red in bud, becoming pink and finally white when fully open. The flowers are so abundant as to hide the twigs and they emit a delicious fragrance. The tiny fruits are yellow with red cheeks and are a first rate bird food.

ALMEY CRAB APPLE, Malus 'Almey'

HOPA CRAB APPLE
Malus 'Hopa'

Like the Japanese Crab, Hopa is one of the most frequently grown and widely planted flowering trees. One of Professor Hansen's originations in South Dakota, it is hardy throughout Zone 4 and well adapted to adverse central plains conditions. The large fragrant flowers are rosy red in color, fading as they mature. These are followed by early ripening fruits, orange with red cheeks and red flesh. When cooked with sugar, these fruits make a delicious spicy jelly with a clear ruby red color, The upright rounded form of the Hopa Crab is adapted to street tree planting, if it is properly trimmed up to give pedestrian clearance.

TEA CRAB APPLE
Malus hupehensis (M. theifera)

This variety is unique among the crab apples because of its very open and picturesque habit of growth. Instead of branching repeatedly to form a bushy head, the branches form only short fruiting spurs along their stems and continue to elongate at the ends. The final effect when in bloom is of long angled branches entirely encased in flowers like floral garlands.

Continued next page

45

The flowers are large, deep pink in bud and white when fully open with a clean fragrance. The fruits are very small, yellow with red cheeks, and a favorite bird food. Because of its open branching habit, the Tea Crab is the best one of all for espalier training flat on a wall.

KATHERINE CRAB APPLE
Malus 'Katherine'

If there is room for only a single crab apple in any garden in Zone 4 or south, this variety would be the choice of many experienced plantsmen. It forms a small rather open branching tree up to 20 ft. in height with good clean foliage and tiny red fruits of great merit as bird food. Its glory lies in the magnificent display of fragrant double flowers, a rich pink like miniature tea roses in bud and a clear sparkling white when fully open. It was named and introduced by the celebrated horticulturist Dr. Donald Wyman, an authority on the crab apple group.

KATHERINE CRAB APPLE, Malus 'Katherine'

PRINCE GEORGES CRAB APPLE
Malus 'Prince Georges'

Here is a greatly superior replacement for the popular double flowering Bechtel Crab Apple with its rich intense fragrance. The large 2 inch flowers of this newer hybrid are even more double than those of the parent variety and come at the same unusually late period, weeks after most other crab apples have long since shed their petals. Hardy in Zone 4, it forms a dense, twiggy and upright crown. Its foliage is far more resistant to leaf spot diseases than other native American crab apples and is retained in humid summers when the former types are badly defoliated. It is well worth planting for its splendid fragrance and unusual period of bloom.

SARGENT CRAB APPLE
Malus sargenti

The dwarf of the crab apple family, this handsome broad growing variety is scarcely larger than a big shrub. The fragrant white flowers are followed by bright red fruits which persist late into the fall until finally stripped off by late migrating birds. In small gardens where there is no room for a larger tree or as a foreground planting in front of larger varieties, the Sargent Crab is indispensible.

REDBUD CRAB APPLE
Malus zumi calocarpa

This dense upright variety, hardy throughout Zone 4 is one of the finest varieties for fruiting effect. It is one of the later blooming varieties, covered with dark pink buds which open to one inch white flowers. The fall fruiting display is particularly fine, as the tiny bright red fruits color up while the leaves are still green and then remain on the plant unblemished late into the winter, creating a lovely effect especially after an early snow storm. They are of a size and persistence that make the Redbud Crab of especial value for wildlife food.

THE FLOWERING CHERRIES

One of the most important of all the groups of flowering trees are the oriental flowering cherries. Each year the famous display of Japanese Cherries planted about the Tidal Basin in Washington, D.C. draws thousands of visitors in early April when the beauty of the trees is reflected in the mirror of the basin. Similarly the flowering of the cherries is the occasion of an annual holiday in Japan particularly around the city of Tokyo where many thousands have been planted. There are few other groups of trees which can match mature oriental cherries in sheer abundance and magnificence of floral display.

There are of course many cherries native to this country and to Europe. Many of them have attractive flowers and subtle beauty of bark and structure, but none of them is comparable to its oriental counterparts for home planting. Consequently we shall only consider the oriental varieties here. These are mostly hardy in Zones 5 and 6, thriving particularly along the east and west coasts and not adapted to the central west from Wisconsin to Idaho. They are often recommended for planting along lakes and streams, but in point of fact they will not grow well in wet soggy soil and thrive in any fertile and reasonably moist garden soil.

As in the case of chrysanthemums and other groups which they have long cultivated, the Japanese have named and at one time or another cultivated a tremendous number of varieties. Over 100 have been named and recorded, and at one time almost half that number were grown in this country. It soon became obvious however, that many of these varieties were so similar that there was no point in growing them all, and the list of species and horticultural varieties described below includes only those of real garden importance. Those interested in more extensive information on this interesting group of flowering trees should look up in a library Paul Russell's excellent *The Oriental Flowering Cherries*, U.S. Department of Agriculture Circular 313, March 1934.

FLOWERING ORIENTAL CHERRIES, Prunus serrulata

AMANOGAWA CHERRY, Prunus serrulata 'Amanogawa'

KWANZAN CHERRY, Prunus serrulata 'Kwanzan'

SARGENT CHERRY
Prunus 'Sargenti'

One of the rarer Oriental cherries, this variety is recommended because it is the hardiest of them all, growing well in Zone 4. The Sargent Cherry is also one of the largest of the cherries, and in its native Japan is an important timber tree and some of the most beautiful furniture is made from its satiny wood. Here in the United States it reaches 50 feet, and is of an upright regular branching habit. In early spring, before the double Japanese cherries bloom, it is covered with single bright pink flowers. In the fall the foliage turns brilliant shades of red, one of the few cherries with first rate autumn color. There is a narrow upright form of the Sargent Cherry, *Prunus sargenti col-*

umnaris, which is most useful to plant where there is not room for a broad tree. Both it and the regular form should be extensively planted as street trees.

AMANOGAWA CHERRY
Prunus serrulata 'Amanogawa'

This is the most narrow and upright of the many Japanese cherries. It forms a tall column of foliage, covered with large, fragrant, pale pink double flowers in May. It is most useful as an accent plant in the garden or as a street tree in very narrow streets where broader growing varieties would be crowded. It is hardy in Zone 6 and parts of Zone 5. The name means "Milky Way" in Japanese, which is an excellent description of the tree in bloom.

48

KWANZAN CHERRY
Prunus serrulata 'Kwanzan'

Justly the most popular of the Japanese Cherries, Kwanzan is the hardiest and most frequently planted of them all. It is of upright branching structure when young, and spreading when mature. With the Yoshino Cherry it comprises the famous cherry planting in Washington, D.C. The rich pink fully double flowers open in May and mature trees are a mass of flowers, their color enhanced and deepened by the copper tints of the unfolding leaves. Kwanzan Cherries are usually grown in the garden with short trunks, but when carefully trained up to give 6 foot clear trunks they make one of the finest small-stature street trees, and an avenue of these can be the most beautiful street imaginable. Kwanzan top-grafted on Mazzard stems makes an unsatisfactory tree however, because the Mazzard is very suscep-

tible to frost cracks and cambium injury and the stem is sometimes killed outright by winter conditions in which Kwanzan trunks are unharmed. In the garden or on the street, the Kwanzan Cherry is in the very first rank as a flowering tree.

SHIROFUGEN CHERRY
Prunus serrulata 'Shiro-fugen'

Here is the most vigorous and the hardiest of the white double flowering Japanese Cherries. It grows almost as tall as Kwanzan but with a more spreading head. The large flowers open white and gradually deepen to a pale pink as they mature, an unusual reversal of the flowering habit of most trees. The bronze new foliage and white flowers create a most unusual and beautiful garden effect. It is hardy in the warmer parts of Zone 5.

SHIRO-FUGEN CHERRY, Prunus serrulata 'Shiro-fugen'

MOUNT FUJI CHERRY, Prunus serrulata 'Shirotae'

SHIROTAE CHERRY (Mount Fuji) Prunus serrulata 'Shirotae'

SHIROTAE CHERRY (Mount Fuji)
Prunus serrulata 'Shirotae'

Mount Fuji is the smallest of the common Japanese cherries, rarely exceeding 15 feet in height. The large double flowers are pale pink in bud but pure white when fully open. It is less hardy than Kwanzan, being reliable in Zone 6. There is no lovelier sight than a mature spreading Mount Fuji Cherry in full bloom, especially in combination with spring bulbs or other flowers.

AUTUMN CHERRY
Prunus subhirtella autumnalis

Here is a semi-double pink form of the Higan Cherry from Japan with a most interesting style of blooming. In the warm days of a prolonged Indian Summer, even after the leaves have fallen, many flowers open up creating a delicate display of flowers when no other trees are in bloom. The main floral display comes in the early spring when the entire dense twiggy crown is concealed with a mass of pink. The Autumn Cherry is a small tree, up to 30 feet tall and thoroughly hardy in Zone 5. It is well worth planting for the delicate beauty of its fall bloom and opulence of its spring display.

WEEPING HIGAN CHERRY
Prunus subhirtella pendula

There are weeping forms of many kinds of flowering trees, but all too many are awkward and grotesque looking, and inferior to upright trees of the same species in blooming qualities as well. A notable exception to this generalization is the Weeping Higan Cherry, often simply known as the Weeping "Japanese" Cherry. This really handsome tree at maturity has long pendulous branches as graceful as a weeping willow and covered in the spring with enormous quantities of single rich pink flowers. It shares the hardiness of the parent Higan Cherry which can be grown safely in Zone 5, farther north than most of the double serrulata cherries. It blooms in early April, one of the first cherries to flower, and lasts a long time if cool windless weather coincides with this period, but shatters quickly in hot windy weather.

There is an excellent double form of the Weeping Higan Cherry, just as graceful, coming into flower a week after the single type and lasting longer. It is in every way the superior of the double weeping serrulata cherry which is stiff and awkward in branching habit.

YOSHINO CHERRY
Prunus yedoensis

This early flowering vigorous cherry forms the main part of the cherry display in Washington, D.C. The single white flowers are borne in great abundance in April. The tree is one of the most rapid growing cherries and soon forms a flat topped, wide spreading tree up to 40 feet in height, and hardy in the southern parts of Zone 5. When trained up to form a straight stem with branches beginning at 6 feet above the ground, the Yoshino makes a beautiful small shade tree, rapid growing when young and adaptable to a variety of soil types. A street of them in full bloom is an unforgettable sight.

WEEPING HIGAN CHERRY, Prunus subhirtella pendula

YOSHINO CHERRY, Prunus yedoensis

THUNDERCLOUD PLUM, Prunus cerasifera nigra 'Thundercloud'   BLIREIANA PLUM, Prunus blireiana

FLOWERING PLUMS

The plums range in size from dwarf prostrate shrubs like the well known Beach Plum to tree forms up to 30 feet in height. They are all beautiful in bloom, their dense, twiggy crowns being hidden in clouds of white, or (rarely) pink, fragrant flowers. The most popular ones for garden planting are those which also have purple foliage, because these are colorful throughout the summer as well as in the flowering period. There are many varieties, several quite similar in appearance, of which the two best ones are described below.

BLIREIANA PLUM
Prunus blireiana (P. veitchi)

Although some of the other purple foliaged plums have a deeper richer color, none of them can match this variety for the beauty of its flowers. These are very double, rich clear pink in color and large for plum flowers, being fully 1 inch across. Because of their good thick petal texture they stand up better to rain and wind than the single plums and are effective longer.

The leaves are a reddish purple and form a pleasing contrast with other green foliaged trees. Like most of the plum trees, this variety grows very rapidly when young but soon slows down to form a neat dense tree, in this case up to 25 feet at maturity. It is adapted to a wide variety of soils and is hardy throughout Zone 5.

THUNDERCLOUD PLUM
Prunus cerasifera nigra 'Thundercloud'

Of all the purple foliaged plums this variety has the deepest richest leaf color, almost a black purple in full sun. Even the wood of the twigs is purple in cross section. The flowers are small, pale pink, and not outstanding, but the deep purple of the foliage is retained unfaded until the leaves drop in the fall. It is hardy in Zone 4 and rapidly develops into an upright densely branched tree up to 25 feet in height. It is much planted as a small street tree in Europe, where the colored foliaged plants are greatly admired.

52

FLOWERING PEARS

There are several varieties of wild pears which produce showy flowers or interesting silvery foliage. These are much more frequently grown in Europe than in this country, but there is one so outstanding that it is rapidly growing in popularity and will soon become one of the important medium sized trees for street tree planting.

BRADFORD CALLERY PEAR
Pyrus calleryana 'Bradford'

Originally imported for fruit breeding work, this species from China soon showed considerable ornamental merit for its masses of white flowers and glossy foliage with brilliant carmine and red autumn color. Wild trees are very spiny when young, but in a block of young seedlings at the USDA Plant Introduction Station at Beltsville, Maryland an unusually straight and vigorous thornless tree was discovered. This was saved, propagated, named for Mr. Bradford, the director of the station, and introduced to the nursery trade.

The Bradford Callery Pear is rapid in growth and forms an upright oval head at maturity. It has two seasons of great beauty, in spring when mature trees are smothered in clouds of white flowers, and again in the fall when the leathery glossy foliage assumes rich tints of carmine and red. The tiny 1/2 inch fruits are relished by birds and do not constitute a litter problem. It is hardy in Zone 4 and adapted to a wide variety of soils, especially stiff clay soils in which few other trees will grow as well. The community of College Park, Maryland has some marvelous street plantings of Bradford Pear, now nearing mature size, and other towns are planting it in many areas.

LE RED FLOWERING PEACH, Prunus persica magnifica

FLOWERING PEACHES

There are many varieties of the domestic peach *(Prunus persica)* which have been selected for ornamental flowers or purple foliage. Some are dual purpose plants with semi-double colorful flowers or purple leaves and bearing juicy edible peaches in the late summer as well.

Of the double flowering varieties grown for their blooms alone, there are double white, rose pink and bright red varieties as well as weeping forms and the interesting 'Peppermint Stick' with double white flowers mottled with pink stripes.

All of them are short lived trees, unfortunately very susceptible to the peach borer insect infestation in the trunk which will speedily kill neglected plants. However they are inexpensive rapid growing little trees up to 20 feet in height and can be replaced if disaster strikes.

53

EUROPEAN MOUNTAIN-ASH, Sorbus aucuparia

THE MOUNTAIN ASHES

This is a group of colorful small trees noted for their large clusters of showy berries but also for their flat heads of white flowers borne in late spring. These are native to the northern hemisphere in North America, Europe, and the Orient, with over a hundred species and varieties known. Some of the finest species occur in the Orient, are little known and still less planted in our streets and gardens, and are perhaps superior to any which are commonly grown. The commoner Mountain-ashes are distinctly northern trees, not thrifty or vigorous south of Zone 6 and many are fortunately at their best in the northern states and Canada where so many attractive southern trees are not hardy.

KOREAN MOUNTAIN-ASH
Sorbus alnifolia

This is one of the best varieties, with dense shiny leaves which are not compound like most of the species but resemble the leaves of certain crab apples. The flowers are pure white, abundantly produced in small clusters like hawthorn flowers and giving rise to masses of bright scarlet berries in the fall. The fall foliage assumes brilliant shades of scarlet and crimson. This variety remains scarce, despite its great merits, because the seed is very difficult to germinate. It reaches 35 feet and is hardy throughout Zone 5

EUROPEAN MOUNTAIN-ASH
Sorbus aucuparia

This is the most commonly grown and popular species and its enormous clusters of bright red berries are most showy when they color up in late summer and early fall. It is hardy north into Zone 3 and thrives especially in Washington, Oregon, and southern Canada. Its great enemies are borer insects which are more serious the further south it is planted.

AMERICAN MOUNTAIN-ASH FRUIT, Sorbus americana

Having been cultivated for so long, it has given rise to many varieties, some with yellow berries, one with doubly cut leaves, and others with distinctive habits of growth.

AMERICAN MOUNTAIN-ASH
Sorbus americana

This native species and the closely related Showy Mountain-ash (Sorbus decora) are the hardiest of the species in this country and grow wild far north into Zone 2 in Newfoundland and Manitoba. They are conspicuous for their large clusters of red fruit, deeper in color than most of the European forms. They are even less tolerant of heat than the two species previously described and belong in the cold region of their origin.

55

COMMON APPLE, Malus pumila 'Red Delicious'

Fruit trees as ornamentals

In the wealth of purely ornamental trees available, people tend to forget that the commercial fruit trees are highly ornamental as well. This is brought forcibly to mind by any spring drive through the orcharding areas of the country, when a field of bright pink peaches or the incredible opulence and fragrance of an old apple orchard in full bloom are so overwhelming.

56

Dwarf trees

In Europe, with its centuries-old traditions of attachment to the soil and frugal independence, suburban homes usually have their fruit trees espaliered on walls in interesting patterns or planted in neat flower and vegetable gardens. In this country too there are many hobbyists who enjoy growing their own fresh fruits in the home garden. The practice has considerably increased since reliable dwarf trees of the common fruits have become available from local nurseries and mail order firms.

In brief, these little trees are produced by grafting standard varieties on special dwarfing root stocks which greatly restrict the growth of the tree and hasten its bearing but which curiously enough develop fruits of fully normal size and flavor. Thus you can see 6 foot specimens of an apple or pear which is normally 40 to 50 feet tall at maturity, loaded with big juicy fruits. Since these dwarfs are growing on restricted root systems they must often be staked to prevent toppling over in wind storms, and of course they are ideal for the fascinating hobby of training them into espalier form against walls or trellises. There are dwarf grafted forms of plums, peaches, apples, and pears and several semi-dwarf cherries available in the nursery trade.

Standard varieties

CHERRIES

Of all the fruit trees for ornamental use the cherries are the most trouble-free. The Pie or Sour Cherries (*Prunus cerasus*) are the best for garden use, being very hardy and not requiring spraying to develop excellent fruits. They flower and begin to bear at an early age and are of course as popular with the birds as with their owners.

The Sweet Cherries (*Prunus avium*) are not as hardy and require a longer time to reach flowering and bearing age. Some varieties are partially sterile, hence several varieties should be planted nearby to insure a good fruit set.

PEARS

The pears *(Pyrus communis)* are adaptable to a wide area of the country and form handsome garden trees with attractive leathery foliage and pure white flowers. The fire blight disease formerly wiped out many pear plantings, but new blight resistant varieties have been developed which are reliable. Pears require little or no spraying for home growing and grow especially well in heavy clay soils. Several varieties should be planted for best pollination.

APPLES

The apple tree *(Malus pumila)* thrives over most of the country from Zone 6 north. It requires much spraying to produce the perfect fruit sold in food stores, but apples entirely satisfactory for home consumption can be produced with a far less rigorous spray schedule. A picturesque gnarled old apple tree is the focal point of many a home landscape design.

PEACHES AND APRICOTS

Commercial peach *(Prunus persica)* production is an exacting science, but isolated little plantings on home grounds also produce plenty of fine fruit with a modicum of care. Peaches and apricots are short lived trees, growing best in Zone 6 and south, and their flowers are exceedingly handsome. The peach borer is their worst insect pest, but it can be controlled by spraying the branches and trunk with DDT when the adult moths are active.

PLUMS

Like the ornamental varieties, the fruiting plums form small, rounded twiggy trees. Several varieties planted near each other give the best pollination, and their fragrant white flowers in early spring are very beautiful. They are hardy in Zone 5 and some varieties grow well further north.

Citrus

In the subtropical part of the United States, principally in those parts of Zones 9 and 10 which lie in Florida, Southern Texas and Southern California, the citrus fruits can be grown for their glossy evergreen foliage and fragrant flowers as well as their colorful fruit. They grow well in acid soils, even in extremely sandy soil which is properly fertilized. Their major enemies are the various scale insects and spider mites, both controllable by careful spraying if they appear. Citrus trees vary in hardiness, some being able to tolerate moderate cold spells which will completely kill others.

There is one curious and very ornamental species, the Hardy Orange — *Poncirus (Citrus) trifoliata* which is deciduous and very hardy. It can be grown along the coasts clear up into the southern part of Zone 5. Although the leathery dark green foliage drops off in the fall, the very thorny twigs are themselves green and attractive in winter. The white flowers appear before the leaves in late April, and the colorful little 2 inch oranges persist on the branches late into the fall. These fruits are too bitter to eat, but having an orange tree in a northern garden is an interesting conversation piece and the tree itself has several seasons of beauty.

SWEET ORANGE, Citrus sinensis

Shade and ornamental trees

THE MAPLES

There is good reason why the Maple Family includes the most popular and frequently planted shade trees. They are adaptable to a very extensive variety of climates and planting conditions. They grow with satisfying rapidity and it is surprising how soon after planting the faster growing kinds develop into sizable specimens. They are easy to move and if properly trimmed at transplanting time (see page 130) and sensibly watered subsequently, losses are negligible. They have good foliage and the fall colors of many kinds are among the best of all trees.

The Maple Family is largely confined to the northern hemisphere. It has a range in size from some of the dwarf forms of the Japanese Maple which are barely 6 feet tall at maturity, up to the Sugar Maple which in the rich coves of the Great Smoky Mountains often exceeds 120 feet in height. Most Maples are very hardy, the majority being reliable in Zone 5 and some of the best natives running on up into Zone 3 in the northern states and Canada. Maples grow vigorously in a broad spectrum of soil types from sandy soils to dense clays and from very acid to decidedly alkaline ones. In general they do best in moderately acid loamy soils, and their fall coloration is considerably enhanced by soil acidity.

This matter of fall color is one which North Americans take altogether too much for granted. One has only to travel in the fall through the wooded areas of New England or Canada with someone from Europe to see the tapestry of autumn foliage through new eyes. Those picture-calendar colors are no exaggeration and are incredible to one accustomed to the muted russets and yellows of an European fall, and in the forefront of the colorful varieties are the Red and Sugar Maples whose leaves light up the woodlands and fence rows like torches. It is with good reason that the maple leaf has been chosen as the symbol of Canada, our sister republic north of the border.

AMUR MAPLE
Acer ginnala

Coming from the forbidding climate of northern China and Manchuria, the Amur Maple is one of the toughest and hardiest of all the family, growing even in Zone 2. It is a dense twiggy plant up to 25 feet in height with fine textured foliage. If grown untouched it usually assumes shrub form with several stems but it can also be trimmed up into standard or tree form. Its winged seeds or keys (samaras) turn red in late summer, contrasting effectively with the green foliage, but its crowning beauty is the fall leaf color, a sharp clear scarlet red. It grows well in dry poor soil or in semi-shade and when left untrimmed it forms a fine tall screening plant. It is an effective substitute for the following variety where the latter is not hardy.

58

BLOODLEAF JAPANESE MAPLE,
Acer palmatum atropurpureum

THREADLEAF OR LACELEAF JAPANESE MAPLE,
Acer palmatum dissectum

JAPANESE MAPLE
Acer palmatum and varieties

Like many other Japanese plant groups which have been grown and appreciated for generations, the Japanese horticulturists have selected a great many named forms of this exceedingly variable little tree. The taller typical forms are all shrub-like when young but form remarkably graceful clumps or small trees up to 20 feet in height when mature. They grow in a wide area up to and including Zone 5 but are at their best in the humid areas along the east and west coasts of this country and Canada. Seedling wild-growing trees have feathery 5 to 9 lobed leaves often red when they unfold, green all summer long, and turning rich shades of orange and scarlet in the fall before they drop.

Of the many named varieties, the Bloodleaf Japanese Maple *(Acer palmatum atropurpureum)* is the most frequently encountered. As

the name suggests, the deep red color of the leaves is retained all summer long, becoming intensified in the fall before the leaves drop off. There are several selections of Bloodleaf Maple being grown, the best of all being the variety "Bloodgood" originally selected by the Bloodgood Nurseries on Long Island. It has the deepest and most fade-proof purple color.

Less common but equally beautiful is the Threadleaf Japanese Maple, *Acer palmatum dissectum*. This is one of the dwarfest forms of the group with filmy, deeply incised foliage like fern leaves, and a graceful weeping habit. The branches of mature specimens are wonderfully twisted and gnarled giving an impression of great antiquity, so necessary for the Japanese style of gardening. There is both a green and a red leafed form of Threadleaf Maple, but the green form appears to have the more durable foliage in hot areas and hence the better appearance throughout the summer.

59

NORWAY MAPLE, Acer platanoides

NORWAY MAPLE
Acer platanoides and varieties

This hardy adaptable tree is one of the most useful of all the trees which have come to us from Europe. It is also an outstanding maple for spring bloom, a mature specimen being covered with a mass of clear chartreuse-yellow flowers creating a most colorful spring picture. It is hardy into Zone 3, tolerates a great variety of soil conditions, and grows rapidly into a spreading rounded tree up to 70 feet in height. The normal spreading forms of the Norway Maple should be trimmed up as high as possible when young, because the branches of mature trees droop with age and their dense shade makes it difficult to grow lawn grass in the area they cover. There are a number of Norway Maple varieties which have been selected and grown, the best of which are briefly described below.

60

COLUMNAR NORWAY MAPLE
Acer platanoides erectum (columnare)

A narrow erect growing variety with branches which turn upwards at the ends parallel to the main trunk. The Columnar Norway Maple at maturity forms a tall rugged column of dark green foliage with a pleasing contrast of light and shadowed areas. Grass will grow right up to the trunk of this splendid variety which many arborists consider to be the best and most adaptable of all columnar trees for planting in narrow streets where space is limited.

CRIMSON KING MAPLE
Acer platanoides 'Crimson King'

This importation from France is the best of all the colored foliage forms of Norway Maple. Its deep purplish red leaf color is retained without fading throughout the summer. It is

COLUMNAR NORWAY MAPLE, Acer platanoides Columna

CRIMSON KING MAPLE, Acer platanoides 'Crimson King'

hardy in Zone 4, much slower growing than the green leafed forms, and is the best purple foliaged shade tree for most of the country.

EMERALD QUEEN MAPLE
Acer platanoides 'Emerald Queen'

A new green leafed form of rapid growth which originated in Oregon. It has a fine upright oval crown like a Sugar Maple and grows vigorously in urban areas where the latter barely exists.

SCHWEDLER MAPLE
Acer platanoides schwedleri

This variety of German origin has bright red leaves in the spring which turn green as they mature in early summer. It is inferior to the Crimson King Maple because the red color is lost so soon, but because of its hardiness (Zone 3) will still be grown in cold areas where Crimson King is often winter killed.

SUMMERSHADE MAPLE
Acer platanoides 'Summershade'
Plant Patent No. 1748

A new upright growing form of Norway Maple with dark green very leathery foliage, highly resistant to scorching injury from hot dry weather. This vigorous variety has proven

to be remarkably well adapted to hot weather in Zone 7 and south where other Norways do not grow well. Grafted improved varieties of all shade trees are far superior to the best strain of seedlings. In any seedling lot there are always a few trees which grow twice as vigorously and may have a markedly improved form. By grafting onto seedling root stocks scions of these occasional vastly superior specimens, it is possible to produce a whole population each identical to the original plant.

SYCAMORE MAPLE
Acer pseudoplatanus

Trees which will grow well at the seashore are not common, and the rapid growing Sycamore Maple is one of the best for this purpose. In hurricane years when trees along the New England coast have been scorched and browned by salt spray, this tree is always conspicuous for its unblemished green foliage. It is hardy in Zone 5 and forms an impressive wide spreading specimen at maturity.

RED OR SWAMP MAPLE
Acer rubrum

The Red Maple has one of the widest ranges of our native trees, growing from eastern and

Continued next page

Plant Pat. 1748
SUMMERSHADE MAPLE, Acer platanoides 'Summershade.'

central Canada to Florida. It has a brilliant red fall color particularly when growing in an area of acid soil. The tiny red fuzzy flowers are one of the earliest spring blossoms, and although individually small are so abundant as to give a fine display. The strains of northern origin are hardy in Zone 3, and southern strains are well adapted to Zones 8 and 9. Because of its adaptability to many soil types, its ease of transplanting, and its colorful flowers and fall foliage, it is a first rate shade tree.

Not all strains of Red Maple are highly colored, and good types are sometimes disappointing in fertile neutral or alkaline soils. The October Glory Maple (Acer rubrum 'October Glory' Plant Patent No. 2116) is a new variety with fine glossy foliage and brilliant red fall color. Most important, this exceptional color is developed in all soil types and planting conditions, a most desirable and unusual quality.

PYRAMIDAL SILVER MAPLE
Acer saccharinum

This maple matures into an upright pyramidal tree of 60 to 100 feet tall and up to 40 feet wide. Its habit of growth produces medium heavy shade. The leaves of this maple are light green above and silvery beneath thus giving rise to its name. The foliage changes to a brilliant yellow in Autumn before falling from the tree. Much finer maples are available for planting in temperate areas, but in dry areas in the Western States and in the harsh climate of Zone 3, this vastly superior form of the tolerant Silver Maple has a place. Its narrow upright branching habit is far more resistant to breakage from ice and wind storms than the typical species. Only bud grafted trees should be planted to secure the valuable narrow shape. As with Red Maple, spring planting is best.

SUGAR MAPLE
Acer saccharum

The largest and finest of our native maples, the Sugar Maple is not only a top notch shade tree, but is also the source of excellent hard lumber. Maple syrup and sugar are made by boiling down the sap, which is tapped as it rises in the early spring. Hardy in Zone 3, it is native from southern Canada and New England south into the Appalachian Mountains

RED or SWAMP MAPLE, Acer rubrum

SILVER MAPLE, Acer saccharinum

of Georgia. It forms a tall oval tree up to 120 feet or more in ultimate height and robed in glowing yellow orange and red fall colors. Its hard springy branches easily survive ice storms which mutilate softer wooded trees. Although it will not stand the polluted atmosphere and pavement glare of city streets, it is a choice shade tree for suburban streets and gardens in eastern Canada, the eastern U.S.A. and in the far Northwest. Some interesting and useful varieties are described below.

COLUMNAR SUGAR MAPLE
Acer saccharum columnare

This fine variety is much more narrow than the typical species and rapidly grows into a narrow oval form most useful for street planting where limited space is a factor, or for creating impressive avenue effects.

SENTRY SUGAR MAPLE
Acer saccharum monumentale

This is one of the narrowest growing shade trees, forming a tall slender column of very dark green foliage with exceptionally fine fall color. It is slow growing but makes a striking landscape accent plant, far more permanent than the popular but short lived Lombardy Poplar.

GREEN MOUNTAIN MAPLE
Acer saccharum 'Green Mountain'
Plant Patent No. 2339

A vigorous new tree derived from crossing the Sugar Maple and closely related Black Maple *(Acer nigrum)* and exhibiting marked hybrid vigor and excellent fall color. The waxy outer coating of its leaves is much thicker than that of ordinary Sugar Maples and for this reason the dark green leaves are unblemished in areas where sun and wind-scorch browns Sugar Maple leaves. It grows into a neat oval shape and is destined to extend the range of the Sugar Maple into hot or dry areas where planting the ordinary type was heretofore impractical.

SUGAR MAPLE, Acer saccharum

63

CUTLEAF EUROPEAN BIRCH, Betula pendula laciniata

THE BIRCHES

The white-barked members of the birch family are among the few trees which everybody recognizes. They are slender and graceful in habit and are planted for ornament rather than shade. Since their main beauty lies in the white trunks, their effect is enhanced by planting them in groups, and clump trees with several stems are especially effective. They are relatively short lived compared to other trees, but their dancing foliage, yellow fall color, and clean white bark make them indispensable ornamental trees for park and garden planting from Zone 6 north to their limits of hardiness.

64

CANOE BIRCH
Betula papyrifera

This native species is the best of the birches for ornamental planting. It reaches 80 feet in the rich woodlands of its native area but is smaller under garden conditions. It is the slowest of the three common species to turn white, but is a pure unblemished chalk white when mature. It is hardy to Zone 2 and is the most resistant of the white barked species to the birch borer, a pest which is troublesome in some cases.

EUROPEAN WHITE BIRCH
Betula pendula (B. alba)

This species is far more beautiful in this country than in its native Europe where its bark is often disfigured by mottling lichens. It is often grown in clump form and commonly reaches 40 feet at maturity. It is hardy to Zone 2. It has been long cultivated and a number of horticultural forms have arisen, among them a narrow fastigiate variety, a dwarf weeping form, and a curious one with purple leaves. The most beautiful variation is the

CUTLEAF EUROPEAN BIRCH
Betula pendula laciniata

This semi-weeping form has deeply incised leaves. It is usually grown as a single trunked tree and forms a delicately graceful lawn specimen.

GRAY BIRCH
Betula populifolia

A small white-barked tree, usually grown with multiple stems, with interesting triangular black patches where each branch enters the main stem. Hardy in Zone 4, the Gray Birch is most effectively planted in groups, especially with an underplanting of spring bulbs which bloom while the foliage is a tender pale green. In some areas the mature leaves are disfigured by the birch leaf miner, an insect which can be controlled by foliar sprays.

THE ASHES

This group of rapid growing shapely trees contains some of the hardiest, most adaptable varieties for shade tree planting. They are not outstanding for fall color but they are vigorous, and easy to transplant. In the north central parts of the west, some of the ashes are among the very few trees which will grow satisfactorily. The most important varieties are as follows.

WHITE ASH
Fraxinus americana

Hardy in Zone 3, rapid growing, and maturing into a shapely oval crown, the White Ash is the best species for fall color. The autumn foliage is yellow, often with an overlay of an unusual deep purple color. Although it is native to the Eastern states, it grows well in the western parts of the country. Top picture.

MARSHALL'S SEEDLESS ASH
Fraxinus pennsylvanica 'Marshall's Seedless'

The Green Ash is our hardiest native species, growing well even in Zone 2. Female plants are often a nuisance in the garden as they seed freely and the young plants sprout abundantly in flower beds and shrub plantings. The Marshall's Seedless Ash, which originated in Nebraska, is a highly superior male tree which bears no seed. It has thick glossy foliage, is a rapid grower, and matures into a fine oval headed tree. This variety is hard to match as a first rate shade tree for northern plain states and other difficult situations. Middle picture.

MODESTO ASH
Fraxinus velutina glabra 'Modesto'

This variety of the Velvet Ash, first extensively planted in Modesto, California, forms a small round headed tree with slender leaflets giving a lacy foliage texture. It reaches 40 feet in height and is, surprisingly enough, hardy in Zone 5 despite its south-western origin. It is excellent for planting in arid desert areas and tolerates soil alkalinity which would be fatal to most other tree species. Bottom picture.

RUBYLACE LOCUST, Gleditsia triacanthos inermis 'Rubylace.'
Plant Pat. 2038

THE LACY HONEY-LOCUSTS

The development from a Cinderella to one of the reigning queens of the shade tree group which has characterized honey-locusts in the past twenty years is due to the foresight of an expert plantsman, John Siebenthaler of Dayton, Ohio. Honey-locusts had long been known for their toughness and adaptability, but were seldom planted because of their dangerous, needle-sharp, branched thorns. With the development and propagation of the Moraine Locust (Plant Patent No. 836) which was both thornless and seedless, a new era of interest in honey-locusts was ushered in.

These new honey-locust varieties have a great many sterling qualities. They are tough and hardy (Zone 4 and south) and they thrive in a wide range of soil types and moisture conditions even in down-town city locations which are lethal to most trees. They have no serious diseases and only one insect pest, the mimosa webworm, which is troublesome in certain

areas in certain years. Their lacy doubly compound foliage is composed of tiny leaflets which when they drop in the fall, sift down into lawn grass and do not need to be raked up. The light dappled shade which they cast is open enough to encourage the growth of desirable lawn grasses but discourages the sun-loving crab grass which is a lawn problem in many areas. The new green leafed varieties have regular crowns of branches rather than the frequently misshapen heads of ordinary seedling varieties. They are in the first rank for large shade tree planting (up to 90 feet at maturity) over much of the U.S.A. and southern Canada except in areas with very acid soil. Brief descriptions of some interesting varieties follow below.

MORAINE LOCUST
Gleditsia triacanthos inermis 'Moraine'
Plant Patent No. 836

The oldest of several new clonal varieties, seedless and thornless, with a wide spreading top at maturity. The parent tree in Dayton is a magnificent specimen.

RUBYLACE LOCUST
Gleditsia triacanthos inermis 'Rubylace'
Plant Patent No. 2038

A slow growing small variety, seedless and thornless. The young foliage is a glowing ruby red color which darkens to bronze green at maturity. Since the tree continues to grow late into the summer a pleasing contrast between the colors of the young and mature foliage persists over a long period.

SHADEMASTER LOCUST
Gleditsia triacanthos inermis 'Shademaster'
Plant Patent No. 1515

Widely planted as a substitute for the American Elm, this thornless variety has the same upright juvenile form and graceful wine glass shape at maturity. Its lush dark green foliage is retained late in the fall after ordinary seedling types have defoliated. It thrives in city conditions as well as suburban areas.

66

MORAINE LOCUST, Gleditsia triacanthos inermis 'Moraine.' Plant Pat. 836

SKYLINE LOCUST Plant Patent No. 1619
Gleditsia triacanthos inermis 'Skyline'

The most upright and narrow crowned of the new thornless honey-locust varieties with dense bright green foliage. Most useful and handsome for planting on narrow streets and where lateral space is limited.

SUNBURST LOCUST Plant Patent No. 1313
Gleditsia triacanthos inermis 'Sunburst'

Most yellow foliaged trees appear sickly and weak under American climatic conditions, but this variety is an exception. The young foliage is a clear golden yellow which darkens to a healthy green color at maturity. Young foliage is produced throughout the summer and the colorful contrast between the young shoots and older foliage creates a sparkling effect as of a flowering tree. It is thornless and seedless.

SUNBURST LOCUST, Gleditsia triacanthos inermis 'Sunburst.'

Plant Pat. 1313

THE MAJESTIC OAKS

Even since primitive man in the north temperate zones began to notice trees, the oaks have been a symbol of strength and durability. The thick trunks and massive limbs of specimens grown in the open form some of the most impressive and awe-inspiring trees. An ancient White Oak near New Brunswick, New Jersey was the inspiration for Joyce Kilmer's well known poem. Because they are so large at maturity, most oaks are not trees for the narrow street or small garden, but wherever there are wide avenues, park areas, or spacious home grounds, oaks deserve first consideration as shade trees. They are popularly thought to be extremely slow growing, but once thoroughly established after transplanting, their rapidity of growth is surprising and quite comparable to many species considered rapid growing.

One of the things which most impresses the European gardeners visiting this country is the great variety of native oaks. Northern Europe has only two species of wild oaks, while a driver in almost any area of the eastern United States will encounter several times that number growing in proximity, and a dozen or more in a single mid-Atlantic state. They range in size from diminutive shrub-like varieties to giants rivaled only by the enormous conifers of the Pacific Coast. The northern varieties are all deciduous, but in the South and in California there are several handsome fully evergreen species. With a very few exceptions, all require a moderately acid soil for best growth, but there are species which will thrive in the soggy clay of swamp lands and others which will do equally well in stony arid soils.

WHITE OAK
Quercus alba

The White Oak is native to the eastern United States and although one of the slowest growing species it is a most impressive wide spreading specimen at maturity, up to 100 feet tall and broader in spread. It is hardy in Zone 4 and assumes rich purple and wine colors in the fall. It is difficult to move and should be transplanted with a ball of earth.

WHITE OAK, Quercus alba

SCARLET OAK, Quercus coccinea

RED OAK
Quercus borealis (Q. rubra)

The Red Oak is a hardy rapid-growing species well adapted to street and home planting from Zone 4 south wherever the soil is on the acid side of neutral. It withstands city conditions better than many other species and the dark red fall foliage is outstanding. It forms a shapely conical tree when young and broadens out into a billowy, rounded crown at maturity, up to 100 feet in height.

SCARLET OAK
Quercus coccinea

Well named the Scarlet Oak, this variety has the most brilliant red fall color of the whole family. It is hardy in Zone 4 and has a feathery and open branching habit casting a lighter shade than other species. It grows best in acid soil and like the White Oak should be moved with a ball of earth. An avenue of Scarlet Oaks in full fall color is an unforgettable sight and the sparkling color is retained long after the leaves of other varieties have faded.

PIN OAK, Quercus palustris

PIN OAK
Quercus palustris

The Pin Oak is the most frequently planted oak species. It is easily transplanted, will grow rapidly in wet or dry soil so long as it is also acid, and has a neat pyramidal habit with gracefully drooping branches. The small fine textured leaves turn red or scarlet in the fall. It is hardy from Zone 4 south. Its graceful shape is unusual in a family noted for rugged picturesque structure at maturity.

WILLOW OAK
Quercus phellos

This is one of the most unusual and beautiful oaks with slender but dense branches and narrow simple leaves like those of a willow tree. It transplants with ease, will thrive in wet soil, but will also grow well on upland sites if the soil is acid. It is hardy in Zone 5 if grown from seed taken from parent trees in the northern limits of its range in New Jersey and eastern Pennsylvania. Trees from more southern sources are hardy only in the more southern portions of Zone 6. The Willow Oak is a most unusual and decorative shade tree.

LIVE OAK
Quercus virginiana

Enormous wide spreading Live Oaks decked with long grey streamers of Spanish "Moss" are one of the most characteristic beauties of the deep south. Up to 70 feet in height and frequently twice as broad, they are one of our most impressive native trees. The Live Oak is evergreen throughout most of its range from Zone 7 south but partially deciduous near its northern limit at Norfolk, Virginia. It is easy to transplant if severely pruned at moving time. Like the equally beautiful California Live Oak (*Quercus agrifolia*) it is well adapted to arid soil. There is a considerable variation in the size and gloss of the foliage and some exceedingly superior specimens are waiting to be selected and propagated by a discriminating plantsman.

CORKSCREW WILLOW, Salix matsudana tortuosa

THE WILLOWS

It must be stated that the willows do not make satisfactory street trees. They have soft fragile wood easily broken by wind or ice storms and even where such conditions are not a problem, they are continually dropping a litter of twigs and small branches. This is not to say that they do not have a very definite place in the landscape, for there is nothing to match the dreamy beauty of a large weeping willow, especially if it is planted beside a lake or stream where its branches can trail over the water. In almost any park or on home grounds where there is plenty of room, especially in a wet area where few other tree species will succeed, there are places where willows are a good choice for planting.

GOLDEN WEEPING WILLOW
Salix alba tristis (Niobe)

This is the hardiest (Zone 2) and in many ways the best of the weeping willows. It has clear golden yellow twigs and young branches which create a colorful effect in the depths of winter when the leaves are gone. The leaves

appear early in the spring and persist late into the fall. They turn a beautiful golden yellow before they drop, which combined with the twig color makes it truly named a golden tree.

BABYLON WEEPING WILLOW
Salix babylonica

The Babylon Willow is the most pendulous of the various weeping types. The branches become very elongated with age often hanging down in straight streamers up to 20 feet in length. It is unfortunately the least hardy of its class being reliable in Zone 6 and southward. Its very narrow leaves create a fine textured effect which enhances the beauty of its long pendulous branches. It is one of the last trees to defoliate in the fall.

THURLOW WEEPING WILLOW
Salix elegantissima

Hardy in Zone 4, this weeping variety is the best replacement for the Babylon Willow wherever it is not hardy. It too has a pronounced weeping habit though not as extreme as babylonica. The leaves are larger and are dropped earlier than the Babylon Willow.

CORKSCREW WILLOW
Salix matsudana tortuosa

This small tree is hardy in Zone 4 and reaches 35 feet at maturity. It has achieved increased popularity with the growth of interest in the Japanese style of gardening. It bears slender pale green leaves on twigs and branches which are curiously twisted and contorted. It makes an interesting "conversation piece" in the garden and the cut branches are most useful for interesting flower arrangements.

A YOUNG BABYLON WEEPING WILLOW, Salix babylor

70

THE FRAGRANT LINDENS

It is certainly true that the finest oak and maple species for home and community planting are of North American rather than European origin, but the reverse is true of the lindens, a family of shade trees prized for their formal outlines and intensely fragrant flowers. All of the best lindens come from Europe and have no serious competitors from this country or the Orient. They have many qualities which recommend them for shade tree planting. They are not fussy about soil conditions, although they will not grow in really arid regions unless irrigated. They have neat attractive heart-shaped leaves, and the better types have formal, regular crowns of foliage. They tolerate atmospheric pollution and other hardships of city life. They have richly fragrant flowers, a very rare attribute in trees hardy in our temperate zone.

LITTLE-LEAF LINDEN
Tilia cordata

This tree is sometimes listed as a "small tree" in tree planting brochures but this is because it grows slowly and densely as a young tree. In

LITTLE-LEAF LINDEN, Tilia cordata

reality it is one of the larger types at maturity. It is one of the very hardiest of the family, being reliable even in Zone 3. It has small dense foliage and in former times was much planted and pruned to make the formal clipped linden allées so popular in 18th century landscape designs. It is especially well adapted to city conditions and is a first choice for this location. Seedling strains of Little-leaf Linden vary greatly, some being excellent but many being so irregular that it is very difficult to match up an attractive street planting. The following variety is the solution to such problems.

GREENSPIRE LINDEN
Tilia cordata 'Greenspire'
Plant Patent No. 2086

This superb new tree is the result of a cross between the best Little-leaf Linden in the Boston Park system and a very fine selection from Germany. It has a perfectly regular upright oval crown, small dark green leaves, and a rapid rate of growth. The fragrance of the small pale yellow flowers is especially fine. Whenever grafted plants of a really superior variety such as the Greenspire Linden are available, it is pointless to plant a seedling grown tree of unknown merit. An orchardist would not dream of planting seedling fruit trees in his orchard, and the final value of a street or garden tree is far in excess of any orchard tree.

CRIMEAN LINDEN
Tilia euchlora

This handsome hybrid linden is hardy in Zone 5, but is also especially tolerant of heat and dry soil. It has glossy bright green leaves from which soot and dust are easily washed off by summer rains which make it an excellent choice for city planting. Like all lindens, it blooms in early summer when most trees have long since flowered. Being a hybrid it does not come true from seed, and grafted trees only should be planted. It reaches 60 feet under favorable growing conditions.

SILVER LINDEN
Tilia tomentosa

The Silver Linden bears dark green leaves which are silver white on their under surfaces, creating a beautiful contrasting effect on breezy days. It grows rapidly to an ultimate height of 80 to 90 feet. The best form of Silver Linden matures with a broad pyramidal crown so regular that it seems to have been tightly sheared. Unfortunately seedling Silver Lindens are extremely variable both in foliage size and color and in habit of growth so only grafted trees should be planted. The 'Princeton' strain is by far the best.

In both this country and Europe, the Silver Linden is one of the most prized trees for planting formal streets.

CHRISTINE BUISMAN ELM, Ulmus carpinifolia 'Christine Bu

SILVER LINDEN, Tilia tomentosa

THE ELMS

Some of the most beautiful and graceful of all our shade trees are members of the elm family. In particular our native American Elm with its distinctive wine glass shape and gracefully drooping outer branches was the favorite variety and was planted by the hundreds of thousands in our towns and cities. Then tragedy struck in the importation of the Dutch elm disease with an insect carrier to spread it on a shipment of veneer logs which entered the country with the bark still adhering to them. Next to the chestnut blight, it was the worst tree scourge ever to strike this continent. From this one introduction it has spread inexorably, decimating or eliminating the elms from a wide area of this country and Canada. Naturally the planting of elms was largely abandoned, and until an immune variety or effective chemical therapy is discovered, the American Elm will never regain its former importance. Research is still being actively pursued, with promising but not conclusive results as yet. The problem may be solved in the future.

72

AMERICAN ELM
Ulmus americana

Growing to 120 feet in height, hardy in Zone 2, and easily transplanted, the American Elm was for generations our most popular shade tree. Its tall arching wine glass shape with pendulous outer branches is unique among shade trees. Many superior varieties were named and propagated by nurserymen during its heyday, the best of them being the variety 'Princeton', with large foliage resistant to insects, pyramidal when young, but ultimately of the finest "elm shape". It is still good for planting in the south or on the West Coast where the two elm diseases do not occur, but the custom of planting entire towns to this one species should never be resumed.

CHRISTINE BUISMAN ELM
Ulmus carpinifolia 'Christine Buisman'

As the name suggests, the Dutch elm disease was first identified in Holland where it ravaged the native population of European elm species. A long and arduous search for a resistant variety was undertaken by Dutch scientists, ultimately resulting in the discovery of this variety named for the distinguished tree pathologist Christine Buisman. It is highly resistant to both Dutch elm disease and Phloem Necrosis and hence is well worth planting. Unfortunately, like other European varieties, it does not have the unique and distinctive wine glass shape of our native species, but it does form a sturdy upright tree to 90 feet in height and hardy in Zone 4. The tree is certainly handsome and combines the other elm virtues of ease in transplanting and rapid growth. Only cutting-grown trees should be planted in order to preserve its prized disease resistance.

CHINESE ELM
Ulmus parvifolia

Though not as hardy as the rather weedy Siberian Elm *(Ulmus pumila)* this handsome variety is a far superior tree. Its tiny dark green

EVERGREEN CHINESE ELM, Ulmus parvifolia sempervirens

leaves remain on the tree late into the fall and turn shades of red before dropping. The bark is shed in patches like a sycamore tree giving an interesting and colorful effect both in the summer and winter. It forms a small round headed tree reaching 50 feet in rich soil and hardy in Zone 5.

An especially interesting evergreen variety, the Evergreen Elm *(Ulmus parvifolia sempervirens)* is hardy from Zone 7 south and is much planted in Southern California although it grows just as well in Florida and Texas too. It is more flat topped than the parent species, with wide spreading branches which weep downward at their tips. Only vegetatively propagated specimens should be planted, as seedlings vary greatly in degree of evergreen character and branching habit.

JAPANESE ZELKOVA

See page 91 for a full description of this valuable close relative of the elms, so similar to them in leaf and habit of growth.

73

THE PALMS

To most gardeners, palms are always associated with the steamy rain-drenched tropics where frosts are unknown and ornamental plantings are rare. Yet many are well adapted to sub tropical regions and thrive in Zone 10 in southern Florida, southern Texas, and along the coast of Southern California up to Monterey. Even more surprisingly one species is remarkably hardy and will grow in the coastal fringe of Zone 8 as far north as southern Virginia and on the west coast to Vancouver Island in British Columbia so that technically speaking, palms can be grown in Canada!

The palms are more ornamental trees than shade trees, although some species have wide spreading crowns of leaves. They vary in height from spreading shrubby varieties to tall trunked sorts 80 or 90 feet tall at maturity. There are some clump varieties with many trunks arising from a central root but the more typical forms are those with single unbranched trunks crowned with the big fountains of leaves which form such imposing avenues in sub tropical city parks and streets.

There are literally hundreds of varieties, mostly tropical and rarely seen outside of botanical gardens and collections. The varieties which follow are only the barest indication of the wealth of plant material available in this enormous family. The best descriptive summary of cultivated palms in English is the special January 1961 issue of the American Horticultural Magazine, which is lavishly illustrated with photographs.

SOUTH AMERICAN JELLY PALM
Butia capitata (Cocos australis)

This vigorous species, also called the Pindo Palm, with its long arching leaves of a silvery grey-green color is the second hardiest species of the various palms. It grows along the east coast from South Carolina south to Florida and on the west coast throughout coastal California. It is a slow growing species which does very well in dry soil. It has very shallow roots and is best planted in a shallow depression which is later filled in as the plant grows taller and more subject to wind throw. It greatly benefits from fertilization just prior to the onset of the growing season.

COCONUT PALM
Cocos nucifera

A picturesque palm hardy only in Zone 10 and south. It grows best along the coast of southern Florida just above the high water mark in soils which appear to be little more than pure sand. No sight is more evocative of the tropical islands than a grove of Coconut Palms beside the seashore, their trunks picturesquely bent and curved by long-past storms and crowned by long arching leaves up to 15 feet in length.

EVERGLADE PALM
Paurotis wrighti

This clump-forming small palm with fan shaped leaves is a native of the Everglades in Florida. It is the handsomest clump palm for the small garden where space is limited. It required abundant moisture to grow well and will thrive in low wet soil where other species languish. It is hardy in Zone 10 up to the lower coastal parts of Zone 9.

SENEGAL DATE PALM, Phoenix reclinata

CANARY ISLAND DATE PALM
Phoenix canariensis

This splendid variety is one of the finest and most handsome species which can be grown in this country. It has a short thick trunk and a huge crown of long graceful leaves. It is hardy in much of Zone 9. Too massive for the smaller garden, it forms an imposing specimen for park or wide avenue planting. Fertilize it liberally for the best leaves.

SENEGAL DATE PALM
Phoenix reclinata

One of the best of the clump-forming palms, forming large clusters of trunks, each crowned by a dense head of drooping leaves. If left untrimmed, a row of this variety makes an impenetrable tall hedge or screen. It is hardy through much of Zone 9 and is being increasingly planted, as the clump forms of trees gain in popularity.

ROYAL PALM
Roystonea regia

This variety is appropriately named the Royal Palm. It is native to a very restricted area of southern Florida, grows to 75 feet in height and is hardy in Zone 10 and south. The leaves drop clean as they die, leaving the gracefully double-tapered trunk clean and clear up to the crown and plume-like leaves. It is a rapid growing species, one of the finest for avenue planting.

CHINESE WINDMILL PALM
Trachycarpus fortunei (Chamaerops excelsa)

This variety from eastern Asia is the hardiest of all palms, being hardy along both the east and west coasts to the limits of Zone 8 as far north as southern Virginia in the east and Vancouver Island in British Columbia. It forms a small dense crown of fan-shaped leaves at the top of a rather slender fibrous trunk. It is a slow growing species, well adapted to a small garden and surviving hostile city conditions of atmospheric pollution and poor soil.

WASHINGTON FAN PALM
Washingtonia filifera

This handsome desert species of palm with fan shaped leaves is native to the canyon country of southern California notably around Palm Springs which was named for a stand which grew there. It reaches 90 feet at maturity, and old specimens have a picturesque thatch of old leaves clothing the trunk. It is hardy in southern Zone 9, and much used for planting in dry soil areas.

MEXICAN FAN PALM
Washingtonia robusta

This species has flat fan shaped leaves of bright green surmounting a slender trunk up to 90 feet in height at maturity. The leaves are not retained as long after they die as the above species. It is hardy in Zone 10, of rapid vigorous growth, and a favorite for planting in the dryer areas of both California and Florida.

MEXICAN FAN PALM, Washingtonia robusta

Additional valuable small trees
DECIDUOUS TREES (Broadleaved)

The main groups or families of small sized or minor ornamental trees (40 feet and smaller at maturity) have been already covered. In addition to these, there are many other beautiful varieties well worth consideration for home planting which are described below, in alphabetical order according to their botanical names. In many cases the tree described is the most handsome one of a more extensive group of similar species, or in a few cases the only one readily obtainable from nurseries. They are arranged for convenience in groups of deciduous broadleaf trees, broadleaf evergreen trees, and coniferous trees. There are many other minor trees useful for home planting. In choosing varieties for home use, the ones described should be given first consideration.

SILK TREE
Albizzia julibrissin

The Silk Tree or Mimosa was originally introduced into cultivation from China, but it has become so widely naturalized in the southern states that it almost seems to be a native. It grows to 35 feet in height and of equal or greater spread. It has lacy twice-compound foliage like fern leaves and bears showy fuzzy pink flowers for a long period in summer. Southern gardeners should plant the blight-resistant varieties 'Charlotte' or 'Tryon' introduced by the USDA after a long search for a reliable tree. Northern gardeners in Zone 6 and the southern part of Zone 5 should plant the hardy form *(A.j. rosea)* introduced by the Arnold Arboretum from the cold part of Korea.

SILK TREE, Albizzia julibrissin

SHADBLOW SERVICEBERRY
Amelanchier canadensis

One of the first of our native flowering trees to bloom in the spring, the Shadblow has other seasons of beauty too. The sweet berries are a favorite June bird food, and the fall color is a rich brocade of orange and red. The white flowers are abundant and borne in drooping many-flowered racemes, and the smooth gray bark is attractive in winter. It can be grown in clump form or trained up with a single trunk to form a neat oval headed little tree. It is hardy in Zone 4 and grows to 30 feet under normal garden conditions. The rare hybrid Apple Serviceberry *(Amelanchier grandiflora)* is even more showy than the parent species.

EASTERN REDBUD
Cercis canadensis

Native to the eastern states from southern Pennsylvania south, this Redbud is hardy to Zone 4 if plants of northern origin are carefully selected. It blooms at the same time as the Flowering Dogwood and its delicate purplish pink flowers form a lovely combination with the white of the dogwood. Out of bloom, its neat heart shaped leaves and spreading habit are also attractive.

There is a variety with pure white flowers *(Cercis canadensis alba)* and one with clear pink flowers, 'Withers' Pink Charm', which are both strikingly beautiful, but rare because they are very difficult to graft. Both are hardy in Zone 5.

RUSSIAN OLIVE
Elaeagnus angustifolia

The Russian Olive is usually grown as a large shrub but can also easily be trimmed up into tree form with a single trunk or picturesque cluster of trunks up to 25 feet in height. It is one of the hardiest of all deciduous trees and thrives even in the harsh climate of the central states and provinces up through Zone 2. Its main attraction is the silvery gray foliage, but the small silvery flowers are very fragrant as well. This tree also gives a good account of itself in some desert and coastal soils.

EASTERN REDBUD, Cercis canadensis

RUSSIAN OLIVE, Elaeagnus angustifolia

CAROLINA SILVERBELL, Halesia carolina

GOLDEN-RAIN TREE, Koelreuteria paniculata

CAROLINA SILVERBELL
Halesia carolina

This beautiful little tree is widely grown and prized in Europe but relatively little known or planted here in the country of its origin. It forms a small arching tree to 30 feet with clean foliage not subject to insect pests or fungi. Its crowning beauty comes in mid-spring before the foliage is fully expanded, when each twig bears a string of little pure white bells along its length, swaying in the breezes like miniature wedding bells. Hardy in Zone 4, the Silverbell does best in reasonably moist soil and benefits from leaf or wood chip mulches.

GOLDEN-RAIN TREE
Koelreuteria paniculata

Hardy yellow flowering trees are rare and summer flowering ones are rarer still. The Golden-rain or Varnish Tree is a popular species for this reason. It is hardy in Zone 5, grows to a rounded 30 feet at maturity, and tolerates a wide variety of soil conditions. The compound foliage is a beautiful coral red color when it unfolds in the spring but has no fall color. The main beauties of the tree are the very large pyramidal clusters of bright yellow flowers effective for a long period in early summer, and the decorative inflated seed pods which turn from pale green through pink to brown as the summer progresses. Unlike Laburnum, it thrives in the South and Midwest.

VOSSI LABURNUM
Laburnum vossi

Though not outstanding out of bloom, this is the most beautiful hardy yellow flowering tree. For a lengthy period in late May it bears long 18 inch tapering clusters of rich yellow pea-shaped flowers exactly like yellow Wisteria flowers. It makes a dense upright vase-shaped tree up to 30 feet in height where the climate is to its liking. It is hardy in Zone 5, but will not stand a hot climate, especially if it is also humid, so that leaf spot diseases can multiply and cause the leaves to drop. It does well in the northeastern states and even better in the Pacific Northwest where the climate is much like that of its ancestral home in England and western Europe. This hybrid tree is greatly superior to either of its parents in size and color of the flower clusters. Illustrated on page 7.

78

CRAPE MYRTLE, Lagerstroemia indica

CRAPE MYRTLE
Lagerstroemia indica

More often thought of as a large shrub than as a tree, the Crape Myrtle is one of the glories of the South. When grown as a clump tree and trimmed up, the smooth mottled bark is conspicuously attractive throughout the year. It is mainly planted for the abundant huge clusters of ruffled flowers displayed for a month or more in late July and August. There are splendid white, pink, red, bluish, and purple varieties varying somewhat in speed of growth and ultimate size. The best red variety is the slow growing, rounded 'Wm. Toovey', and the best pink is the brilliant 'Ingleside Pink'. It is hardy in Zone 7 and south in both the east and west coast states and across the lower portion of the country. Old specimens reach 25 feet in height. It is in the very first rank of choice for a dependable small tree in the South.

SORREL TREE
Oxydendrum arboreum

The Sorrel Tree or Sourwood reaches 70 feet in height in rich forest soil in the southern Appalachian mountains, but under ordinary garden conditions it is a small pyramidal tree to 40 feet at maturity. It is hardy to the southern part of Zone 4, but will stand considerable heat. Like azaleas and rhododendrons, it must have an acid soil to succeed, and grows well in humusy soil.

There have been many arguments as to which is our most beautiful native American small flowering tree. Many insist it is the white dogwood, but many more hold out for the Sorrel Tree. It is constantly a beauty, starting with the translucent amber red of the young leaves as they unfold in the spring, continuing with the big pendulous sprays of white flowers like Andromeda flowers borne for a long period in July, and finishing with the brilliant scarlet color of the lustrous foliage in autumn. The Sorrel Tree is light and feathery, more of an Oriental looking "character tree" than a shade tree, and its delicate and enduring beauty is best enjoyed at close hand in intimate association with a terrace or patio.

AMUR CORK TREE
Phellodendron amurense

This is an excellent small tree for city planting, with glossy compound foliage and interesting rugged corky bark. The branches are thick and picturesquely twisted. The Amur Cork Tree is one of the extremely limited list of trees which can be depended upon to prosper in a city garden in Zone 3.

SORREL TREE, Oxydendrum arboreum

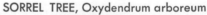

CHINESE PISTACHE
Pistacia chinensis

Hardy in Zone 9, the Pistache is a colorful small tree which performs well in the hot dry soils of Florida and Southern California. The foliage is compound and fine textured rather like Sumac leaves, and turns spectacular shades of red for a long period in the fall. It has beeen in cultivation in this country for a long time but is only now beginning to gain real popularity. Non-fruiting male trees should be grafted for street tree planting. It reaches 40 feet under ordinary soil conditions.

JAPANESE STEWARTIA
Stewartia pseudocamellia

It is unfortunate that this tree was not given a good descriptive common name when it was introduced to the western world, for it is one of the really choice small flowering trees. Pyramidal in shape and hardy in Zone 5, Stewartias are deciduous hardy members of the Camellia Family, and the large single white flowers of this species with their golden centers certainly resemble single Camellias. The flowers are abundant, and open for a long season of bloom in late June and July. The foliage is neat and attractive, turning shades of crimson and purple in the fall. The colorful flaking bark of older specimens is ornamental during the winter months when the leaves have dropped to reveal it. Here is a garden gem for acid soil regions of the East and West Coast which will grow in sun or shade and exhibit some feature of beauty twelve months out of the year.

JAPANESE STEWARTIA, Stewartia pseudocamellia

JAPANESE SNOWBELL
Styrax japonica

Even without its floral display, the Japanese Snowbell would be a worthy tree for the small garden because of its neat, fine textured dark green foliage and zig-zag branching habit. It is a "clean tree" without insect pests or leaf diseases. It becomes an object of rare beauty in late spring when even the smallest twigs bend beneath the weight of thousands of pendant white star shaped flowers, each with a golden center. It is often grown in clump form. As a mature specimen there is no small tree more beautiful or permanent in the home landscape from Zone 5 south.

JAPANESE TREE LILAC
Syringa amurensis japonica

This tree out of bloom looks more like a cherry than a lilac, except for its opposite leaves. It grows to 35 feet, is hardy in Zone 4, and was more frequently planted at the turn of the century than now. Its flowers open at a desirable time in mid-June, are individually small and white in color, but are borne in enormous pyramidal trusses 6 to 8 inches in height and spread. It is a good tough flowering tree for cold climates and central regions where many others are not hardy.

JAPANESE SNOWBELL, Styrax japonica

EVERGREEN TREES (Broadleaved)

COOTAMUNDRA WATTLE
Acacia baileyana

The Wattles comprise an enormous family of Australian desert woody plants ranging in size from tiny prostrate shrubs to 60 foot trees. They share in common deeply incised fern-like foliage and feathery yellow flowers, many very fragrant. The Cootamundra Wattle grows very rapidly to a 30 feet height and equal spread, and is hardy in Zone 10. It has fine textured silvery foliage and is a mass of fragrant yellow flowers for weeks in the late winter and spring. It stands extremely dry soil and is a favorite California yard and street tree.

SILVER WATTLE
Acacia decurrens dealbata

This is the hardiest (Zone 9) and one of the most vigorous Wattles, reaching 50 feet in its native Australia. It is well adapted to the hot Deep South, grows very rapidly and is covered each spring with millions of clear yellow fragrant flowers. The feathery bluish green foliage is attractive throughout the year.

STRAWBERRY TREE
Arbutus unedo

This slow growing evergreen tree is often grown in shrub form in the acid soils of the Pacific Coast. Its lustrous 3 inch leaves and striped red and dark brown bark are effective throughout the year, while brilliant orange red strawberry-like fruits color the tree from October to January.

ORCHID TREE
Bauhinia variegata

This is a small (to 20 feet) slow growing tree hardy only in Zone 10 which is a favorite in southern Florida and California for its large 4 inch lavender flowers which resemble florists' Cattleya Orchids. It forms an umbrella-shaped head and blooms profusely in the late winter. There is also a white flowering variety 'Candida' which makes a lovely companion plant for the purple form. Both forms keep their curious two lobed leaves all winter and shed them only as the flowering season begins, after which a new crop is promptly grown.

COOTAMUNDRA WATTLE, Acacia baileyana

PURPLE ORCHID TREE, Bauhinia variegata

WHITE ORCHID TREE, Bauhinia variegata 'Candida'

CAROB , Ceratonia siliqua

LOQUAT, Eriobotrya japonica

SHOWER OF GOLD
Cassia fistula

This spectacular flowering tree is popular for planting in Zone 10, where it takes the place of Laburnum. It has large pinnate foliage retained most of the year, and in early spring is densely hung with 18 inch racemes of bright canary yellow flowers like a yellow Wisteria in effect. It slowly grows into a rounded tree to 30 feet in height with spreading branches which droop at the ends. It is adapted to a wide variety of soils and of arresting beauty when covered with long sprays of flowers each spring.

CAROB
Ceratonia siliqua

This glossy evergreen tree for Zone 10 thrives in dry soil areas and makes a top notch shade tree for home garden or avenue planting. It grows to 40 feet in height with a 30 foot spread, and is a standard avenue tree in coastal southern California. The seeds and sugary pulp of this tree are eaten in the Mediterranean area, and it is often called St. John's Bread because legend has it that this was the "locust" on which John the Baptist lived during his sojourn in the wilderness.

82

LOQUAT
Eriobotrya japonica

This 20 foot evergreen tree is hardy in Zone 7 and gives a lush tropical appearance to many gardens in the mid south, both east and west. The long 8 inch leathery leaves are boldly handsome and its orange yellow quince-like fruits are an added beauty in late spring. They are also edible, with a tart refreshing flavor. The best specimens are those growing in full sunlight in mellow, well fertilized soil.

CALIFORNIA HOLLY (Toyon)
Heteromeles arbutifolia

One of the most spectacular fruiting plants for the sub tropical areas of Zone 8, this handsome glossy leafed evergreen is often grown as a clump with several picturesquely angled trunks. Its greatest beauty is in the late fall when it is densely covered with big clusters of glowing scarlet berries, much used for Christmas decorations. It will not stand wet soil and should be planted in full sun for the best display of berries.

ENGLISH HOLLY
Ilex aquifolium

There is some doubt as to whether the English Holly should be classified as a "small tree" since it ultimately exceeds 40 feet in height. However it is slow growing enough to be so considered for practical gardening purposes. Although it is hardy in Zone 6 and south, it does not grow nearly as well as the native American Holly in the eastern states and in many such areas is temperamental and unreliable. The picture is reversed on the West Coast where it grows to perfection in the cool moist belt which extends far up into British Columbia. Wherever it can be grown, its fine glossy foliage and the densely clustered berries on female plants outshine even the best forms of American Holly. Since flowers of the two sexes are borne on separate plants, a male plant must be growing in the vicinity if the females are to bear fruits. There are a number of desirable horticultural forms varying in fruiting, leaf size, shape and color. These as well as a wealth of other Ilex species are described and illustrated in Harold Hume's excellent book *Hollies*.

TOYON or CALIFORNIA HOLLY, Heteromeles arbutifolia

ENGLISH HOLLY, Ilex aquifolium

GLOSSY PRIVET
Ligustrum lucidum

The botanists have admirably succeeded in their apparent life-work of muddying the waters of plant nomenclature by switching the botanical name of this plant with another similar variety enough times to leave everybody thoroughly bewildered! With a little special trimming up this, the tallest of the privets, can be grown into a first rate trouble-free evergreen tree, 30 feet in height and hardy in Zone 7 and south. Its fine glossy 5 inch foliage and dense crown merit far wider use as a small tree for street or landscape planting. It is adaptable to a wide range of soils and will stand city conditions.

OLIVE
Olea europaea

From Zone 9 south, especially in dry areas of the West Coast, the Common Olive makes a picturesque evergreen tree with a dense bushy head and attractively gnarled branches. It is one of the oldest of all cultivated trees and was grown for its fruits from earliest Biblical times all round the Mediterranean Sea. It makes a first rate ornamental tree, and a sparse or non-fruiting variety would make a fine street tree.

CHINESE PHOTINIA
Photinia serrulata

This vigorous broadleaf evergreen is often grown as a shrub frequently cut back to keep it within bounds, but it is even more handsome when grown as a multiple stemmed small tree. Under such treatment it reaches 35 feet in height and is handsome at every season of the year. In the spring the red new growth contrasts with the shiny dark green older foliage. It is covered with 6 to 8 inch flat clusters of white flowers in May and with bright red clusters of berries in the fall. Hardy in Zone 7 and south, grows best and most densely when planted in full sun in well drained soil.

COMMON OLIVE, Olea europaea

CONIFEROUS TREES

WESTERN RED-CEDAR
Juniperus scopulorum

EASTERN RED-CEDAR
Juniperus virginiana

These two very similar trees are here considered together as they are almost identical in landscape effect. The western species is well adapted to the western and plains states south to Mexico and is exceedingly drouth resistant, but makes a very unthrifty plant in the East. It is particularly liable to produce blue foliaged seedlings, the best of which have been named and propagated for sale. It is hardy from Zone 4 south.

The eastern species is the hardier plant, growing up into Zone 2 in parts of Canada. It is normally dark green in color, but blue forms are also known and propagated. It is adapted to a remarkably wide range of soil types and is native from Canada to Florida. The local races from Virginia south are broader and more loosely branched and make graceful slow-growing feathery trees. The northeastern form is narrow and densely columnar and makes a thick, long-lived screening plant. Female trees bear every second or third year heavy crops of beautiful blue berries which are a favorite winter bird food.

DARK AMERICAN ARBOR-VITAE
Thuja occidentalis nigra

This variety of the popular American Arbor-vitae is far superior to the general run of seedling origin plants because it retains its rich dark green color in winter, when most other strains and varieties develop a brown protective pigment in the leaves. It requires a reasonably moist soil to grow well but is extremely hardy (up into Zone 2 in the eastern third of

WESTERN RED CEDAR, Juniperus scopulorum

Canada). Untrimmed, it develops into a tall broad-based pyramidal tree, ultimately to 60 feet in height but only after 40 or 50 year's growth. It can be maintained at a much smaller size by shearing, and it makes one of the finest tall evergreen hedges for screening or privacy, with much less trimming required than other evergreen trees.

DARK AMERICAN ARBOR-VITAE, Thuja occidentalis nigra

Some outstanding large trees

In addition to the bigger groups and families of large or major trees (40 feet and larger at maturity) which have already been discussed, there are a number of other varieties of great importance for home and community planting. These are described below, in alphabetical order according to their botanical names, and arranged in groups composed of deciduous broadleaf trees, broadleaf evergreen trees and coniferous trees with needle-like leaves. In some cases they are the only member of their families with great ornamental merit, and many other cases they are the best representatives of a large family which contains many other species which are desirable ornamentals. The total of these various lists by no means covers all of the tree species and varieties potentially usable for home or street planting. There are a number of books which describe them in considerable detail, in the very first rank of which is Donald Wyman's excellent *Trees For American Gardens*. Getting to know trees in intimate detail is a rewarding hobby with unlimited horizons for the home gardener.

BRAZILIAN PEPPER, Schinus terebinthifolius. See page 94

DECIDUOUS TREES (Broadleaved)

RUBY HORSE-CHESTNUT
Aesculus carnea briotti

This excellent large tree with its bold tropical-appearing foliage and bright red flowers borne in big upright clusters up to 9 inches in length is comparable to the handsomest of the tropical flowering trees when in bloom in May. It is hardy in Zone 3, and grows very slowly to an ultimate height of 70 feet in rich soil. Its dark green leaves are compound, with five spreading leaflets like the fingers of a hand. This tree and its relatives look best in the cool humid areas of the northeast and northwestern states and the adjacent provinces of Canada. South of Zone 6 the foliage suffers from heat and a rust fungus in many areas. It is the first choice among the various horse-chestnuts to consider for home planting.

CHINESE CHESTNUT
Castanea mollissima

Since our indigenous American Chestnut was wiped out of its native range by a blight accidentally imported from the Orient, many

people have thought it is no longer possible to grow the fruiting chestnuts. This species from China has withstood the blight for countless generations since both come from the same area, and is highly resistant to it. It forms a dense rounded tree much like a big apple tree in shape and soon begins to bear large sweet nuts in abundance each fall. It is hardy in Zone 5, and prefers acid soil. Several trees should be planted together for pollination. More of these trees should be planted so that our children can enjoy the pleasures of gathering and roasting chestnuts in the fall as our grandparents used to do.

KATSURA TREE
Cercidiphyllum japonicum

This neat clean tree from Japan is planted for its attractive heart shaped foliage which turns orange and scarlet in the fall. It is hardy to Zone 4 and reaches 70 feet in height in this country. The leaves do not seem to be attacked by insect pests or fungus diseases, but will scorch from the summer heat on trees growing in dry soils or under city conditions. Its neat oval crown and graceful foliage are a handsome addition to the garden or park.

YELLOW-WOOD
Cladrastis lutea

Trees with really fragrant flowers are rare in our climate, and this splendid native species with its long racemes of pure white flowers like white wisterias is one of the best. It is hardy in Zone 4, and although slow growing, ultimately reaches 60 feet in height. It requires a rich neutral soil for best growth. It has smooth grey bark like a beech and forms a rounded head of compound foliage which turns a clear yellow color in the fall. A single blooming specimen of this lovely tree will fill a large area with its rich penetrating fragrance.

RUBY HORSE CHESTNUT, Aesculus carnea briotti

EUROPEAN BEECH
Fagus sylvatica

Although our native American Beech has the paler, more beautiful bark, the European Beech is the more commonly planted. This is because the seed is readily available from commercial dealers and because a number of very distinctive and beautiful forms have been selected in nurseries and propagated by grafting onto seedling roots. The common European Beech, though very slow to develop when young, makes a big oval tree up to 80 feet high in this country. It is hardy in Zone 4 and prized for its smooth grey bark and glossy dark green foliage. The two following ones are the most beautiful of the horticultural forms.

RIVER'S PURPLE BEECH
Fagus sylvatica riversi

Most horticulturists consider this tree to be the most beautiful of all purple foliaged trees. There are several purple beeches grown but this River's variety with its exceptionally large leaves of a rich deep purple color is the most spectacular form. It is slender and slow in developing when young, but ultimately makes a huge dense specimen tree. Like all beeches it thrives best in the eastern states and provinces north of Zone 7 and in the Pacific Northwest.

PURPLE BEECH, Fagus sylvatica riversi

WEEPING BEECH
Fagus sylvatica pendula

It may be stated unequivocally that this magnificent, slow growing, hard wooded tree is the best of all weeping trees. It is awkward looking when young, but forms an enormous mounded mass of gracefully pendant branches and clean dark green foliage when mature. An old tree is broader than tall, and fully grown specimens sometimes cover nearly an acre of ground. It is obviously not a tree for a small yard, but wherever a cool temperate climate and sufficient space permit its best development, no more beautiful tree can be planted.

GINKGO
Ginkgo biloba

Sometimes called the Maidenhair Tree, this ancient species is one of the oldest kinds of tree still growing today. Fossil leaves preserved in rock formations show that it was growing even as far back as the Jurassic period 10 million years ago, and was once a common tree in North America and even in Greenland! Almost extinct in the wild, it was preserved and revered in Chinese monastery grounds for countless centuries. It appears to have outlived its insect pests and fungus diseases and is now remarkably free from both today. It is also very tolerant of adverse city conditions. It is hardy in Zone 4, grows in a variety of soils, and forms a huge picturesque tree at maturity with an open branching habit and clear canary yellow fall color. The Ginkgo, like hollies, has flowers of one sex only on each tree. The female or pistillate trees bear round orange fruits like large cherries with an ill-smelling pulp surrounding the seed, and only grafted male or staminate trees should be planted as these bear no fruits.

In addition to the normal spreading forms, narrow fastigiate types called the Sentry Ginkgo are also common. The best of these are propagated by grafting. The narrow forms, contrary to old theories, may be of etiher sex, so only male plants should be propagated.

GINKGO, Ginkgo biloba

KENTUCKY COFFEE-TREE
Gymnocladus dioica

This interesting large tree with its thick twigs and large doubly compound leaves is valuable for creating a tropical effect in northern plantings. It is very open in branching and does not suffer from ice storms which play havoc with dense twiggy trees. It grows to 90 feet and is hardy in Zone 4 and far into the south. The large oval seeds were said to have been roasted and used as a coffee substitute in Colonial times.

SWEET-GUM
Liquidambar styraciflua

The Sweet-gum with its regular pyramidal outline and bold star-shaped foliage is one of the best trees for autumn color, turning rich shades of crimson to purple in the fall. It is native to a wide range of the eastern third of the United States from New Jersey and central Illinois south to Florida and Texas. Only trees of northern origin should be planted in the northern sections, as southern forms are much less hardy. The Sweet-gum is hardy in parts of Zone 4, reaches 100 feet at maturity and grows especially well in California and Oregon as well. Its symmetrical beauty is an asset to the home grounds and as a street tree.

TULIP TREE
Liriodendron tulipifera

This is the largest of the trees native to the eastern states, approaching the size of redwood trees when growing in the rich coves of the Smoky Mountains. It forms a broad pyramidal head up to 150 feet tall and has broad 4-pointed leaves and large tulip-shaped greenish yellow flowers in June, each petal having an orange blotch at its base. It is obviously not a tree for the small garden or narrow street, but makes a magnificent specimen from Zone 4 south wherever there is room for it.

The Tulip Tree (sometimes called Yellow Poplar) is related to the magnolias and like them is much more easily transplanted in the spring, since its fleshy roots are easily injured and slow to recover.

SWEET-GUM, Liquidambar styraciflua

89

BLACK TUPELO
Nyssa sylvatica

This handsome ornamental tree is native from Maine and southern Ontario south to the Gulf of Mexico. Hardy in Zone 4 (trees of northern origin only) and growing to 80 feet in rich soil, it grows well in wet clay soil where most other trees will languish. Its clean lustrous foliage, glowing orange to scarlet fall color, and neat pyramidal habit give it first rate ornamental qualities. It is unfortunately very difficult to transplant, and balled and burlapped young trees or better still container-grown trees should be planted, preferably in the spring. Like so many trees with a very great native range, those grown from southern seed are not hardy in the north but are the best forms for southern planting.

LONDON PLANE TREE
Platanus acerifolia

This is one of the oldest of the hybrid trees, a cross between the tender Oriental Plane and our hardy native Sycamore. It is hardy in Zone 5, reaches 100 feet in rich soil, and is one of the mere handful of trees which will survive under extreme city conditions with their poor soil, limited moisture, and toxic atmosphere. The foliage resembles large maple leaves but develops no fall color. The bark flakes off in patches revealing the olive or yellowish younger bark beneath. Like other trees with attractive bark, the London Plane Tree is especially handsome when grown in clump form with several trunks arising from a single root system.

AMERICAN SYCAMORE
Platanus occidentalis

While not adapted to city conditions, our native Sycamore is most handsome in the rural areas where it grows well. The bark flakes off in large patches revealing younger under-bark which is often pure white in certain local strains. It grows to enormous size, up to 150 feet in rich lowland soil, and is native to the eastern half of the United States from extreme southern Canada to Texas. It is hardier than the London Plane, growing throughout Zone 4. Its large maple-like leaves and beautiful mottled bark make it well worth planting around country homes and farms.

AMERICAN SYCAMORE, Platanus occidentalis

LOMBARDY POPLAR, Populus nigra italica

LOMBARDY POPLAR
Populus nigra italica

This extremely narrow columnar tree forms a beautiful spire of foliage especially in Italy and southern France, where ancient specimens line many a picturesque road. It is hardy up into Zone 2, but unfortunately in most parts of this country is subject to a canker disease which kills it before it reaches maturity. It is much planted as a very rapid-growing narrow screen to hide unsightly views, but (we hope) with the knowledge that it is not permanent and will ultimately have to be replaced, either by a new planting or by more permanent but slow growing screening trees planted beside it.

JAPANESE PAGODA TREE
Sophora japonica

This large rounded tree with dark green compound foliage is unusual for its summer blooming season. The large trusses of pale yellow-white pea shaped flowers open in mid July and continue on into August. It is hardy in Zone 4, but will stand a hot dry climate just as well. It is exceptionally well adapted to city conditions and in increasing favor because its tiny leaflets do not require raking up and disposal. This variety and the Shademaster Locust are the two main varieties being planted in the city of Paris in France today. A native Sophora reaches 75 feet in height and may have an equal spread. One of the largest trees in this country is on the island of Nantucket, where it was apparently brought from the Orient and planted by a sailing ship captain.

REGENT PAGODA TREE
Sophora japonica 'Regent'
Plant Patent No. 2338

The Japanese Pagoda Tree varies greatly in habit of growth, some specimens being very contorted or almost weeping in shape. Hence it is most difficult to match up an avenue of seedling trees. The Regent Pagoda Tree is a vigorous growing, upright variety only recently introduced to the nursery trade. It must be propagated by grafting on seedling rootstocks in order to perpetuate its marked resistance to leaf hopper feeding, its rapid development into a tall oval-crowned tree, and its exceptionally glossy dark green foliage. Its flower trusses are remarkable for their size and lasting bloom.

JAPANESE ZELKOVA
Zelkova serrata

This close relative of the elms greatly resembles them in leaf and branching habit. Most importantly, it is not susceptible to the Dutch elm disease. It is hardy in Zone 5 and south and in its native Japan makes an enormously tall timber tree over 100 feet in height. In this country however it does not grow as tall and slowly develops into a shapely rounded tree with sharply ascending branches which curve outward at the tips. Unlike elm foliage, Zelkova leaves turn attractive shades of maroon and russet in the fall.

VILLAGE GREEN ZELKOVA
Zelkova serrata 'Village Green'
Plant Patent No. 2337

This new tree is the result of a long search to find a hardier form of Zelkova with a habit of growth which duplicates that of our native American Elm. It has large handsome foliage and, as its name suggests, the lovely arching wine glass shape of the vanished elms which once shaded many a beautiful New England village "green" or park. This variety survived unharmed, a winter which killed all other Zelkovas to the ground in a northern nursery.

JAPANESE ZELKOVA, Zelkova serrata

EVERGREEN TREES (Broadleaved)

CAMPHOR TREE
Cinnamomum camphora

This handsome round-headed tree with glossy evergreen foliage is much planted in Florida, along the Gulf of Mexico and in Southern California. It is slow growing and neat, reaches 50 feet at maturity, and is hardy in Zone 9. Camphor is distilled from the leaves and small twigs, which readily give off its odor when bruised. The pea-sized shiny black berries are relished by birds who have spread the seed and naturalized the tree in many southern areas. Picture at left.

EUCALYPTUS

There are hundreds of species of Eucalyptus in their native Australia and over 50 are being grown in nurseries today. They are very rapid growing evergreen trees which thrive in arid areas and tolerate alkali soils. They are so widely planted in southern California as to appear almost to be a native tree. Many however are weedy in appearance, with weak wood and wide-ranging greedy roots.

CRIMSON EUCALYPTUS
Eucalyptus ficifolia

This is one of the most popular of its family for ornamental planting because of its brilliant crimson to scarlet flowers. It is hardy in Zone 9 and reaches 50 feet in height, thriving in hot dry areas and alkali soil. Seedlings of this variety vary in the intensity of flower color and vegetatively propagated plants of the best colored strains should be planted.

TASMANIAN BLUE EUCALYPTUS
Eucalyptus globulus

The Blue Gum, as it is also called, is the most frequently planted species of the whole family. It has long slender evergreen leaves and grows rapidly into a tall narrow-headed tree up to 100 feet in height. At maturity, it has a smooth pale grey bark. It thrives in most of California and in Zone 9 throughout the southwest. The narrow leaves of mature trees are up to 12 inches in length but those Juvenile shoots are rounded and bluish in color, frequently sold by florists as decorative foliage.

INDIAN LAUREL FIG
Ficus retusa

This is one of the best of the various rubber trees for ornamental planting. It is hardy in Zone 9 and rapidly grows into a large specimen up to 50 in height and 30 feet across, densely clothed in dark green evergreen foliage. It can be easily confined to a smaller space by restrictive pruning.

MORETON BAY FIG
Ficus macrophylla

This handsome Australian evergreen tree, like our native Live Oak, grows broader than high. A mature tree will reach 70 feet in height and 150 feet in spread, so it is not a tree for the small yard! Nevertheless it is excellent for a park tree in Zone 10 and its handsome 10 inch evergreen leaves are enhanced by a glossy upper surface.

INDIAN LAUREL FIG, Ficus retusa

AMERICAN HOLLY, Ilex opaca

SHARPLEAF JACARANDA, Jacaranda acutifolia

AMERICAN HOLLY
Ilex opaca

Our native American Holly is often wrongly considered a small tree because it is so slow in growth, but at maturity it forms a big dense-headed tree 60 feet in height and often nearly as broad. The spiny evergreen leaves and colorful red berries are the traditional symbol of Christmas and extensively used for wreaths and house decorations at that season. It is hardy in Zone 5 and requires rich acid soil for best growth. It is far better adapted to our American growing conditions than the more handsome English Holly which is virtually confined to the Pacific Northwest as an ornamental tree.

Hollies, like ginkgos and willows, are unusual in that the two sexes of flowers are borne on separate trees. The female when pollinated become the prized long-lasting red berries. Hence the presence of a male (staminate) tree in the vicinity is necessary for the pollination of female (pistillate) trees in order to produce fruits. Unless you are certain that other male hollies are growing in the area, be sure there is at least one male in any clump you plant.

94

SHARPLEAF JACARANDA
Jacaranda acutifolia

This is one of the finest evergreen trees for sub-tropical conditions (Zone 10). It grows into an open, spreading crown of very finely cut fern-like foliage covered in early summer with enormous trusses of 2 inch lavender blue flowers shaped like trumpet flowers. It is extremely popular for garden and street planting in Florida and southern California.

BRAZILIAN PEPPER TREE
Schinus terebinthifolius

This rapid growing evergreen with abundant compound leaves thrives in dry soil areas throughout Zone 10. Its masses of bright red berries are conspicuous throughout much of the winter, giving rise to the common local name of Christmas-berry. It reaches 45 feet in height, with a rounded crown and long gracefully drooping branchlets and fine textured foliage. Its abundant crop of berries makes it an excellent tree to attract birds. It grows in arid areas with alkaline soils where many other trees will not thrive.

CONIFEROUS TREES

The following varieties represent only a very small portion of the coniferous trees well adapted for ornamental planting in home grounds and park lands. The planting of collections of the tree-sized forms has much declined as the big estates have been broken up and sold. However there is room for slow growing species even in relatively small gardens. The use of conifers for shade trees has actually greatly increased, especially in the southeastern states where many new housing developments have been built in thinned-out woods of native pines. Such semi-shaded yards are ideal sites for growing healthy plantings of the camellias and azaleas for which the South is famous.

Evergreen and deciduous conifers should be more frequently planted as community street trees, trimmed up to give vehicular and pedestrian clearance. Such evergreen plantings are majestic and permanent, but they should not be installed where winter snows are routine because they retain their foliage all winter, casting a dense shade which causes patches of snow and ice to persist long after the rest of the street is clear.

For tempering cold prevailing winter winds and for permanently screening out unsightly views and buildings, the coniferous evergreens are of course unexcelled.

ATLAS CEDAR
Cedrus atlantica

This rapid growing, majestic evergreen from northern Africa is hardy in Zone 6 and reaches 100 feet in height at maturity. Like all of the true cedars, its needles are borne in little tufts at the end of short spurs on the branchlets, making a most picturesque foliage effect. The tree is distinctly pyramidal when young, but wide spreading with unique tiered flat branches at maturity. Seedling grown trees vary in foliage color from green to shades of blue.

BLUE ATLAS CEDAR
Cedrus atlantica glauca

This is the best blue needled form of the Atlas Cedar, perpetuated by grafting branches onto seedling trees. Wherever it can be grown, it is the best of all the blue foliaged conifers, far more shapely and permanent at maturity than the various blue spruces. It makes an impressive flat-topped wide-spreading specimen tree at maturity and the cut foliage makes decorative arrangements in the house. It is hardier than most forms of the parent species and can be grown in protected southern parts of Zone 5.

DEODAR CEDAR
Cedrus deodara

The Deodar comes from the Himalaya Mountains of India and is only hardy from Zone 7 south. It is more graceful and also much more rapid growing than the above varieties. Many plantsmen consider it to be the best big conifer for the hot portions of the south where spruces, firs, and hemlocks all languish in the heat. Its needles are longer than those of other true cedars thus giving the impression of denser branches. The central "leader" and branch ends are pendulous in young trees giving lacy and graceful effect.

BLUE ATLAS CEDAR, Cedrus atlantica glauca

DAWN REDWOOD
Metasequoia glyptostroboides

This is a narrow growing deciduous conifer which drops its graceful fern-like foliage in the fall and grows a new set each spring. It is hardy in Zone 6 and the southern portion of Zone 5 and grows to 80 feet at maturity. Long known only as a fossil tree from rocks of the Mesozoic era, to the astonishment of botanists it was discovered growing in a small remote area of China. It was introduced by the Arnold Arboretum which received a shipment of seeds before China turned communist, and generously sent them to botanical gardens all over the world. Aside from its fascinating history, it is an ornamental of considerable merit with beautiful pale green foliage, colorful reddish bark, and a very rapid rate of growth.

The variety 'National' introduced by the National Arboretum in Washington, D.C. is a distinctive Metasequoia which grows into a very narrow regular spire, superior to a great many irregular seedling forms.

DAWN REDWOOD, Metasequoia glyptostroboides

NORWAY SPRUCE
Picea abies (P. excelsa)

There are a great many species of spruces, many of which make fine ornamentals, but none of them is as widely adaptable to diverse soils and climates as the Norway Spruce. It is hardy from Zone 2 south to Zone 7, the southern limit of the area in which it grows well, and reaches 140 feet at maturity in this country. Much criticism has been heaped on this species, but it is still the standard by which other species may be judged. It has a very large native range in Europe and many local strains exist which vary enormously. Some are poor and thin foliaged, but the best form majestic spires of thick dark green foliage borne on gracefully pendulous branches.

CANARY PINE
Pinus canariensis

Among the pines, unlike the firs and spruces, there are species for every kind of climate and exposure in this country, from north to south and from the seaside to the high mountains. There is not room to describe them all and only the best species for the north and south are given here.

DEODAR CEDAR, Cedrus deodara

The Canary Pine is a tall slender variety with lustrous drooping needles 9 to 12 inches long. It is hardy in Zone 8 and thrives in hot climates and dry soil. It grows rapidly when young and forms a round but open-headed tree up to 80 feet tall. A first rate evergreen for many of the southern states and California.

WHITE PINE
Pinus strobus

This magnificent tree up to 100 feet in height and native to eastern Canada and the U.S.A. is considered by many to be our most beautiful native pine. It is hardy in Zone 3, densely pyramidal when young, but open and picturesque with a flat top and irregular branches when mature. It is easy to transplant and may be restrained and kept small and dense for many years by careful pruning. Its beautiful form at all stages of growth and its soft eternally green needles make it first choice for planting in gardens north of Zone 7.

DOUGLAS FIR
Pseudotsuga taxifolia (P. douglasi)

This important and beautiful conifer resembles a spruce in superficial habit and foliage. Its soft closely-set needles are retained on the tree for many years, giving it a dense bushy top. There are three distinct strains varying in hardiness and rapidity of growth. The only one for most of the country outside of the Pacific Northwest is *P. t. glauca,* the Rocky Mountain form, slow and dense in growth and completely hardy in Zone 4. It is one of the finest of our native evergreens for gardens.

CANADA HEMLOCK
Tsuga canadensis

The Canada Hemlock is one of our most beautiful native evergreen trees for garden planting. It grows in a regular pyramidal form with graceful horizontal branches, drooping at the tips and bearing dense flat sprays of short needles. It is native to eastern Canada and the United States and is hardy from Zone 3 south through Zone 7, below which the summers are too hot for its liking. If left untrimmed, this hemlock makes a stately specimen up to 90 feet in height. Because of its small twigs and fine texture, it is extremely well adapted to hard shearing and is easily trained into a thick hedge which can be maintained at a very slowly increasing height for decades.

ORWAY SPRUCE, Picea abies   EASTERN WHITE PINE, Pinus strobus   DOUGLAS FIR, Pseudotsuga taxifolia

Trees listed by flower color

TREES WITH WHITE FLOWERS

SHADBLOW SERVICEBERRY	**Amelanchier canadensis**
APPLE SERVICEBERRY	**Amelanchier grandiflora**
STRAWBERRY TREE	**Arbutus unedo**
WHITE ORCHID TREE	**Bauhinia variegata candida**
CHINESE CHESTNUT	**Castanea mollissima**
WHITEBUD	**Cercis canadensis alba**
CITRUS FRUITS	**Citrus species**
YELLOW-WOOD	**Cladrastis lutea**
FLOWERING DOGWOOD	**Cornus florida**
JAPANESE DOGWOOD	**Cornus kousa**
PACIFIC DOGWOOD	**Cornus nuttalli**
DOWNY HAWTHORN	**Crataegus mollis**
DOUBLE WHITE HAWTHORN	**Crataegus oxyacantha plena**
WASHINGTON HAWTHORN	**Crataegus phaenopyrum**
CAROLINA SILVERBELL	**Halesia carolina**
TOYON	**Heteromeles arbutifolia**
GLOSSY PRIVET	**Ligustrum lucidum**
YULAN MAGNOLIA	**Magnolia denudata**
SOUTHERN MAGNOLIA	**Magnolia grandiflora**
STAR MAGNOLIA	**Magnolia stellata**
SWEET BAY	**Magnolia virginiana**
ARNOLD CRAB APPLE	**Malus arnoldiana**
SIBERIAN CRAB APPLE	**Malus baccata**
JAPANESE FLOWERING CRAB APPLE	**Malus floribunda**
TEA CRAB APPLE	**Malus hupehensis**
COMMON APPLE	**Malus pumila**
SARGENT CRAB APPLE	**Malus sargenti**
REDBUD CRAB APPLE	**Malus zumi calocarpa**
SORREL TREE	**Oxydendrum arboreum**
CHINESE PHOTINIA	**Photinia serrulata**
HARDY ORANGE	**Poncirus trifoliata**
THUNDERCLOUD PLUM	**Prunus cerasifera 'Thundercloud'**
SHIROFUGEN CHERRY	**Prunus serrulata 'Shirofugen'**
MOUNT FUJI CHERRY	**Prunus serrulata 'Shirotae'**
YOSHINO CHERRY	**Prunus yedoensis**
BRADFORD CALLERY PEAR	**Pyrus calleryana 'Bradford'**
COMMON PEAR	**Pyrus communis**
JAPANESE PAGODA TREE	**Sophora japonica**
MOUNTAIN-ASH	**Sorbus — all species**
JAPANESE STEWARTIA	**Stewartia pseudocamellia**
JAPANESE SNOWBELL	**Styrax japonica**
JAPANESE TREE LILAC	**Syringa amurensis japonica**

TREES WITH PINK FLOWERS

SILK TREE . . . . Albizzia julibrissin varieties
WITHER'S PINK REDBUD. . . . . Cercis canadensis 'Withers' Pink Charm
RED FLOWERING DOGWOOD. . . . . Cornus florida rubra
TOBA HAWTHORN . . . . Crataegus mordenensis 'Toba'
INGLESIDE CRAPE MYRTLE . . . . Lagerstroemia indica 'Ingleside Pink'
SAUCER MAGNOLIA . . . . Magnolia soulangeana
KATHERINE CRAB APPLE. Malus 'Katherine'
PRINCE GEORGES CRAB APPLE. . . . . Malus 'Prince Georges'
BLIREIANA PLUM . . . . Prunus blireiana
PEACH . . . . Prunus persica
SARGENT CHERRY . . . . Prunus sargenti
AMANOGAWA CHERRY . . . . Prunus serrulata 'Amanogawa'
KWANZAN CHERRY . . . . Prunus serrulata 'Kwanzan'
AUTUMN CHERRY . . . . Prunus subhirtella autumnalis
WEEPING CHERRY . . . . Prunus subhirtella pendula

TREES WITH RED FLOWERS

RED MAPLE . . . . Acer rubrum varieties
RUBY HORSE-CHESTNUT . . . . Aesculus carnea briotti
CAROB . . . . Ceratonia siliqua
PAUL'S SCARLET HAWTHORN. . . . . Crataegus oxyacantha pauli
CRIMSON EUCALYPTUS . . . . Eucalyptus ficifolia
RED CRAPE MYRTLE . . . . Lagerstroemia indica 'Wm. Toovey'
ALEXANDRINA MAGNOLIA . . . . Magnolia soulangeana 'Alexandrina'
ALMEY CRAB APPLE . . . . Malus 'Almey'
CARMINE CRAB APPLE . . . . Malus atrosanguinea
HOPA CRAB APPLE . . . . Malus 'Hopa'

TREES WITH BLUE AND LAVENDER FLOWERS

PURPLE ORCHID TREE . . . . Bauhinia variegata
SHARPLEAF JACARANDA . . . . Jacaranda acutifolia

TREES WITH YELLOW FLOWERS

COOTAMUNDRA WATTLE . . . . Acacia baileyana
SILVER WATTLE . . . . Acacia decurrens dealbata
NORWAY MAPLE . . . . Acer platanoides varieties
SHOWER OF GOLD. . . . . Cassia fistula
GOLDEN-RAIN TREE . . . . Koelreuteria paniculata
LABURNUM . . . . Laburnum vossi
TULIP TREE . . . . Liriodendron tulipifera
LINDENS . . . . Tilia species (pale Yellow)

BLOOMS OF SILK TREE. See page 76

BLOOM OF TULIP TREE. See pages 15-89

BLOOMS OF CRIMSON EUCALYPTUS. See page 93

BLOOMS OF ARNOLD CRABAPPLE. See page 44

BLOOMS OF PURPLE ORCHID TREE. See page 81

AMERICAN HOLLY. See page 94

FRUIT and BLOOMS of STRAWBERRY TREE. See page 81

The fruiting varieties of trees deserve consideration for their extra ornamental value. A few produce fruit palatable to humans and many provide food for birds. See page 106 for a list of trees producing conspicuous fruit.

SIBERIAN CRAB APPLE. See page 44

LEMON. See page 57

Summer leaf color in trees

The green color in tree leaves is caused by the presence of countless microscopic bodies within the leaf cells called chloroplasts. They contain the remarkable green organic compound called chlorophyll. This unique compound has the ability to combine water and carbon dioxide and, by utilizing the energy of sunlight, create simple sugars. We and all other higher animals are ultimately dependant upon this process for the food we live on. It seems deceptively simple. It occurs constantly all around us throughout the long summer days, and yet *exactly* how it is accomplished remains a baffling mystery.

Very rarely in nature, certain abnormal tree specimens occur which have red rather than green leaves. This aberration is due to the occurence in the sap of the plant leaves of excessive amounts of red sugar compounds called anthocyanins which are so intense as to mask the green chlorophyll that is also present as in normal trees. The anthocyanins are manufactured in the leaves themselves, so that red foliaged twigs or buds, even when grafted on normal green seedlings, still give rise to red trees. This characteristic makes it possible to reproduce an infinite quantity of red trees originating from one single exceedingly rare seedling sport. It is curious and inexplicable that red-foliaged sports or mutations have been discovered in a large variety of trees of European origin such as Norway Maple, English Oak, European Birch, Sycamore Maple, European Beech, plums and many others. Yet although our native North American trees have been observed and grown in great quantities for generations, red leafed mutations are exceedingly rare and only a handful have turned up. In any case, the red-leafed condition is apparently disadvantageous to trees or shrubs, and most red forms are much slower growing and smaller at maturity than their normal green-leafed counterparts.

Blue-foliaged trees occur in a number of coniferous or needle leafed evergreens as well as such sub-tropical trees as the Wattles (*Acacia*) and some Eucalyptus. This bluish color is usually due to a frosty waxy coating or "bloom" that covers the leaf or needle surface, which is a normal green color beneath this superficial coating. If a twig of Colorado Blue Spruce or Blue Atlas Cedar is dipped in boiling water, the wax is melted and the color of the needles instantly turns bright green. It is also gradually washed off by repeated rains and snows. Consequently blue-foliaged conifers exhibit their most spectacular color in the early summer, just after the new growth has taken place, and are least distinctive in the spring after a full year's wear has removed a large portion of the wax.

Trees with yellow foliage in the summer, even under optimum growing conditions, are also aberrant specimens which are simply deficient in chlorophyll so that the carotin normally present in all leaves shows through more fully than normal. Such trees, with few exceptions such as the Sunburst Locust, do not look well under our hot North American summer climate and soon appear sickly and often scorched. In the cooler and often foggy European climate, they are more attractive. Even there, they are rather unhealthy looking compared to normal green-foliaged trees. Europeans think more highly of colored foliaged plants than we, and yellow-leafed forms of English Oak, European Beech, Norway Maple, Sycamore Maple, and many other trees are by no means uncommon in England and on the Continent.

The following lists cover some of the more handsome forms of trees with colored foliage during the summer months, or, in the case of evergreens, throughout the year.

Trees with unusual summer foliage color

TREES WITH BLUISH FOLIAGE

COOTAMUNDRA WATTLE . . . . **Acacia baileyana**
SILVER WATTLE. . . . . **Acacia decurrens dealbata**
BLUE ATLAS CEDAR . . . . **Cedrus atlantica glauca**
BLUE GUM . . . . **Eucalyptus globulus**
RED CEDARS . . . . **Juniperus scopulorum** — some forms
　　　　　　　　　　　　　　　　　　Juniperus virginiana — some forms

TREES WITH RED TO PURPLE FOLIAGE IN SUMMER

BLOODLEAF JAPANESE MAPLE. . . . **Acer palmatum atropurpureum**
CRIMSON KING MAPLE. . . . . **Acer platanoides 'Crimson King'**
SCHWEDLER MAPLE . . . . **Acer platanoides schwedleri**
RIVER'S PURPLE BEECH. . . . . **Fagus sylvatica riversi**
RUBYLACE LOCUST. . . . . **Gleditsia triacanthos inermis 'Rubylace'**
BLIREIANA PLUM. . . . . **Prunus blireiana**
THUNDERCLOUD PLUM . . . . **Prunus cerasifera nigra 'Thundercloud'**

TREES WITH SILVERY OR GREYISH FOLIAGE

SOUTH AMERICAN JELLY PALM
(Pindo Palm). . . . . **Butia capitata**
RUSSIAN OLIVE. . . . . **Elaeagnus angustifolia**
COMMON OLIVE. . . . . **Olea europaea**

Fall color in trees

The annual miracle of fall coloration when leaves which have been a constant shade of green throughout the summer rapidly turn yellow, red, or purple, is a phenomenon which never ceases to amaze the thoughtful observer. The complex organic chemistry involved is not thoroughly understood even now, but the general process is known. The over-lying cause is a combination of steadily decreasing day length as the days shorten into fall, and the cooling of the temperature. The interaction of these forces causes the deciduous tree to stop growing and convert a layer of cells at the base of each leaf stem into corky cells which will prevent water loss after the leaf has dropped. The formation of this corky layer gradually stops up the microscopic pipe lines which all summer supplied water and mineral material to the leaf. As the leaf activity diminishes, the chlorophyll which gave it its green color all summer is no longer manufactured. Chlorophyll is a very unstable chemical which must be constantly renewed by the active leaf, and consequently it rapidly disappears when this activity dwindles. A very stable bright yellow or orange pigment called carotin is also present in the leaf throughout the summer, but its presence is masked by the more abundant and dominant chlorophyll. As the leaf dies, the chlorophyll rapidly disappears but the more stable carotin lingers on, no longer concealed, to give to Norway Maple, ginkgos and birches, for example, their brilliant yellow fall colors.

The formation of red and purple colors is more complicated than the simple unmasking of the yellow pigments. These deeper and richer hues are due to the presence in the cellular sap of a sugar compound called anthocyanin. This substance is dissolved in the sap itself; and in acid cellular sap such as that contained in Tupelo, Scarlet Oak and Flowering Dogwood leaves, turns a glowing red. In the more alkaline sap of White Ash trees for example it turns purple or plum color. The acidity of

FALL FOLIAGE COLOR VARIATIONS OF SWEET-GUM. See page 89

the cellular sap in some species such as Red Maple is partially dependant upon the soil in which the tree is growing. Thus the leaves of Red Maples growing in very acid soils turn a brilliant red, whereas the same trees growing in a neutral or slightly alkaline soil will be a rather disappointing yellow. Red Maples specially propagated for their striking red color like the October Glory Maple are red in any soil in which the tree will thrive. The buildup of the color-giving red anthocyanins is caused by the same gradual stoppage of the pipe lines leading into the leaf which also causes yellow coloration. In this case the leaf continues for a while to manufacture sugar and anthocyanin which cannot get out of the leaf and through interaction with the leaf sap assumes the brilliant red tints. The same phenomenon can be observed in mid-summer if a twig or branch is choked off by a wire or by an injury removing the bark. Here too the passage of sugars away from the manufacturing location is stopped, excesses build up, and the leaves turn red. Girdling a branch by removing a ring of bark is sometimes done to create especially red apples for exhibition and competitions.

FALL FOLIAGE COLOR OF BLOODLEAF JAPANESE MAPLE. See page 59

These trees should be planted for their brilliant fall color effects.

TREES WITH PURPLE FALL FOLIAGE COLOR

WHITE ASH......................Fraxinus americana
SWEET-GUM ....Liquidambar styraciflua (some trees)
WHITE OAK ....Quercus alba
COMMON PEAR..................Pyrus communis
JAPANESE STEWARTIA...........Stewartia pseudocamellia

TREES WITH YELLOW FALL FOLIAGE COLOR

NORWAY MAPLE.................Acer platanoides varieties
SUGAR MAPLE..................Acer saccharum (some trees)
BIRCHES ....Betula species
REDBUD ....Cercis canadensis
YELLOW-WOOD ....Cladrastis lutea
GINKGO ....Ginkgo biloba
TULIP TREE ....Liriodendron tulipifera
LOMBARDY POPLAR ....Populus nigra italica
GOLDEN WEEPING WILLOW ......Salix alba tristis (Niobe)

TREES WITH RED FALL FOLIAGE COLOR

JAPANESE MAPLE...............Acer palmatum varieties
RED MAPLE ....Acer rubrum
OCTOBER GLORY MAPLE ....Acer rubrum 'October Glory'
SUGAR MAPLE..................Acer saccharum (some trees)
SHADBLOW SERVICEBERRY ......Amelanchier canadensis
FLOWERING DOGWOOD ....Cornus florida
JAPANESE DOGWOOD ....Cornus kousa
PACIFIC DOGWOOD ....Cornus nuttalli
WASHINGTON HAWTHORN ....Crataegus phaenopyrum
SWEET-GUM ....Liquidambar styraciflua
BLACK TUPELO................Nyssa sylvatica
SORREL TREE ....Oxydendrum arboreum
CHINESE PISTACHE ....Pistacia chinensis
BRADFORD CALLERY PEAR ......Pyrus calleryana 'Bradford'
RED OAK.......................Quercus borealis
SCARLET OAK..................Quercus coccinea
PIN OAK.......................Quercus palustris
KOREAN MOUNTAIN ASH ....Sorbus alnifolia

FALL FOLIAGE COLOR OF WASHINGTON HAWTHORN. See page 38

FALL FOLIAGE COLOR OF OAK VARIETIES. See pages 68-69

FALL FOLIAGE COLOR OF GINKGO. See page 88

Trees with conspicuous fruits

TREES WITH RED FRUITS

STRAWBERRY TREE. . . . .**Arbutus unedo**

FLOWERING DOGWOOD . . . .**Cornus florida**

JAPANESE DOGWOOD . . . .**Cornus kousa**

PACIFIC DOGWOOD . . . .**Cornus nuttalli**

DOWNY HAWTHORN . . . .**Crataegus mollis**

WASHINGTON HAWTHORN. . . . .**Crataegus phaenopyrum**

TOYON . . . .**Heteromeles arbutifolia**

ENGLISH HOLLY . . . .**Ilex aquifolium**

AMERICAN HOLLY . . . .**Ilex opaca**

ALMEY CRAB APPLE . . . .**Malus 'Almey'**

SIBERIAN CRAB APPLE . . . .**Malus baccata**

HOPA CRAB APPLE. . . . .**Malus 'Hopa'**

COMMON APPLE . . . .**Malus pumila**

SARGENT CRAB APPLE . . . .**Malus sargenti**

REDBUD CRAB APPLE . . . .**Malus zumi calocarpa**

CHINESE PHOTINIA . . . .**Photinia serrulata**

BRAZILIAN PEPPER TREE. . . . .**Schinus terebinthifolius**

MOUNTAIN-ASH . . . .**Sorbus species**

TREES WITH BLUE OR PURPLE FRUITS

SERVICEBERRY . . . .**Amelanchier species**

WESTERN RED-CEDAR. . . . .**Juniperus scopulorum**

EASTERN RED-CEDAR . . . .**Juniperus virginiana**

BLACK TUPELO . . . .**Nyssa sylvatica**

TREES WITH YELLOW FRUITS

CITRUS FRUITS. . . . .**Citrus species**

LOQUAT . . . .**Eriobotrya japonica**

HARDY ORANGE. . . . .**Poncirus trifoliata**

JAPANESE PAGODA TREE. . . . .**Sophora japonica** (Pale Yellow)

Trees with especially ornamental bark

Variety		Bark Characteristics
RED MAPLE	Acer rubrum	Smooth, gray (on younger branches)
SHADBLOW SERVICEBERRY	Amelanchier canadensis	Smooth, gray
STRAWBERRY TREE	Arbutus unedo	Striped red and brown
CANOE BIRCH	Betula papyrifera	Chalk white
EUROPEAN BIRCH	Betula pendula	White
GRAY BIRCH	Betula populifolia	White, black marking under limbs
YELLOW-WOOD	Cladrastis lutea	Smooth, gray
TOBA HAWTHORN	Crataegus mordenensis 'Toba'	Olive, "muscular" appearance
BEECHES	Fagus species	Smooth, gray
CRAPE MYRTLE	Lagerstroemia varieties	Mottled green and gray
SAUCER MAGNOLIA	Magnolia soulangeana varieties	Smooth, gray
AMUR CORK TREE	Phellodendron amurense	Ridged, corky
LONDON PLANE TREE	Platanus acerifolia	Mottled olive
AMERICAN SYCAMORE	Platanus occidentalis	Mottled white
ROYAL PALM	Roystonea regia	Smooth, cement-like
GOLDEN WEEPING WILLOW	Salix alba tristis	Yellow (on smaller branches)
JAPANESE STEWARTIA	Stewartia pseudocamellia	Mottled, flaking

EUROPEAN BIRCH   BEECH   AMUR CORK TREE   JAPANESE STEWARTIA

THE DEEPLY ENGRAVED TEXTURE OF NATIVE DOUGLAS FIR BARK CONTRASTS AND COMPLIMENTS
THE FALL COLORS OF VINE MAPLE FOLIAGE.

BOLD DESIGNS AND COLORS OF EUCALYPTUS TREE BARK HARMONIZES BEAUTIFULLY WITH THE
ARCHITECTURAL FORMS AND RED HUES OF BRICK AND TILE.

Climate and trees

No one knows exactly why one species of tree is of "iron-clad" hardiness and another from the same genus is easily susceptible to winter injury. Even more fascinating is the question of why plants from the same species can differ so enormously in hardiness. Basically the cause seems to lie in their geographical point of origin. Differences in hardiness between populations from the northern and southern extremes of the native range of a species have been detected in most tree species. In species such as the Yellow-wood *(Cladrastis lutea)* with a very limited native range, these differences are minute. In species with an enormous range — the Red Maple *(Acer rubrum),* for example, which is native from southern Florida to Newfoundland — there is a great variation in hardiness. Trees grown from Southern Florida seed are scarcely hardier than palms; trees from Canadian seed are perfectly hardy in Zone 3.

These differences are obvious adaptations to the climate in which the parent trees are growing. They are expressed in many ways. Trees from northern limits of their range, even when planted farther south, are slow to leaf out in the spring and they stop growing early in the fall. Usually they are slower and more compact in growth, and have harder wood. Generally in a given area it is best to plant trees of the local strain native to that area or somewhat north of it.

In the list of especially hardy trees which follows, plants grown from northern seed are always recommended.

There are other factors beside latitude which influence hardiness. The most obvious is altitude. Very roughly, each 100 foot rise in the altitude of a planting site is equivalent to a 60 mile move to the north. To cite an extreme example, at the tops of the higher peaks in the Great Smoky Mountains of Tennessee many trees such as Balsam Fir and Red Spruce are found growing wild just as they do in Canada, even though they are entirely absent in most parts of the intervening 900 miles.

Another basic factor determining hardiness is proximity to large bodies of water which act as gigantic thermostats in moderating climatic extremes. It is well know that many woody plants can be grown commercially close to the south shore of Lake Erie near Cleveland, Ohio, though they will not survive on inland locations south of the lake. A glance at the map of Hardiness Zones of the United States and Canada on page — shows how markedly the warmer zones curve upward and north along both the Atlantic and Pacific coastlines.

Even more important in hardiness is what is called the micro-climate of the planting site itself. It is quite possible to grow most trees considerably north of their limits of field hardiness by planting them in sheltered sunny spots where they are protected from harsh winter winds by buildings or dense evergreen plantings. Conversely, it is possible to grow desirable trees of northern species south of their native areas by planting them in cool locations with a northern exposure, shaded by tall trees from the full heat of the sun.

Bowl-shaped areas surrounded by higher ground on all sides are known as "frost pockets" in areas with severe winters. Cold air is heavier than warm air. It runs down hill and settles in low areas, especially those with no exit. In such a local area, the flowers of the Saucer Magnolia, for example, will be damaged by late frosts every spring. The same trees planted in a higher area nearby will be entirely uninjured under exactly the same weather conditions.

The hardiest tree species described in this book are listed alphabetically by botanical name on the following page. Zone given indicates the normal northern limits for the species yet the same tree is adaptable to warmer zones.

These are the hardiest trees described in this book.

TREES HARDY IN ZONE 2

(Winter temperatures dropping to from —35° to —50° F.)

AMUR MAPLE . . . .**Acer ginnale**

CANOE BIRCH . . . .**Betula papyrifera**

EUROPEAN BIRCH . . . .**Betula pendula varieties**

RUSSIAN OLIVE. . . . . **Elaeagnus angustifolia**

MARSHALL'S SEEDLESS ASH. . . . . . .**Fraxinus pennsylvanica 'Marshall's Seedless'**

EASTERN RED-CEDAR . . . .**Juniperus virginiana**

SIBERIAN CRAB APPLE. . . . .**Malus baccata**

NORWAY SPRUCE. . . . .**Picea abies**

LOMBARDY POPLAR . . . .**Populus nigra italica**

GOLDEN WEEPING WILLOW . . . .**Salix alba tristis**

AMERICAN MOUNTAIN-ASH . . . .**Sorbus americana**

SHOWY MOUNTAIN-ASH. . . . .**Sorbus decora**

DARK AMERICAN ARBORVITAE . . . .**Thuja occidentalis nigra**

AMERICAN ELM . . . .**Ulmus americana**

PRINCETON ELM . . . .**Ulmus americana 'Princeton'**

TREES HARDY IN ZONE 3

(Winter temperatures dropping to from —20° to —35° F.)

NORWAY MAPLE (except 'Crimson King') . . . .**Acer platanoides varieties**

RED MAPLE . . . .**Acer rubrum**

SILVER MAPLE. . . . .**Acer saccharinum pyramidale**

SUGAR MAPLE. . . . .**Acer saccharum varieties**

RUBY HORSE-CHESTNUT. . . . .**Aesculus carnea briotti**

TOBA HAWTHORN . . . .**Crataegus mordenensis 'Toba'**

WHITE ASH. . . . .**Fraxinus americana**

COMMON APPLE. . . . .**Malus pumila**

AMUR CORK TREE. . . . .**Phellodendron amurense**

WHITE PINE . . . .**Pinus strobus**

SOUR CHERRY. . . . .**Prunus cerasus**

EUROPEAN MOUNTAIN-ASH . . . .**Sorbus aucuparia**

LITTLE-LEAF LINDEN. . . . .**Tilia cordata**

GREENSPIRE LINDEN . . . .**Tilia cordata 'Greenspire'**

THESE NATIVE HAWTHORNS AND OAKS ADD BEAUTY TO A NEW HOME WHILE OFFERING THE
ADDED ADVANTAGES OF MATURE SIZE AND WINTER HARDINESS.

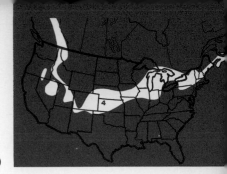

TREES HARDY IN ZONE 4

(Winter temperatures dropping to from —10° to —20° F.)

CRIMSON KING MAPLE............Acer platanoides 'Crimson King'
OCTOBER GLORY MAPLE.........Acer rubrum 'October Glory'
SHADBLOW SERVICEBERRY.......Amelanchier canadensis
APPLE SERVICEBERRY.............Amelanchier grandiflora
GRAY BIRCH.....................Betula populifolia
KATSURA TREE..................Cercidiphyllum japonicum
EASTERN REDBUD...............Cercis canadensis
YELLOW-WOOD ....Cladrastis lutea
FLOWERING DOGWOOD...........Cornus florida and plena
DOWNY HAWTHORN..............Crataegus mollis
ENGLISH HAWTHORN............Crataegus oxyacantha varieties
WASHINGTON HAWTHORN........Crataegus phaenopyrum
EUROPEAN BEECH...............Fagus sylvatica varieties
GINKGO.........................Ginkgo biloba varieties
HONEY-LOCUST ....Gleditsia triacanthos varieties
KENTUCKY COFFEE-TREE.........Gymnocladus dioica
CAROLINA SILVERBELL...........Halesia carolina
WESTERN RED-CEDAR.............Juniperus scopulorum
SWEET-GUM ....Liquidambar styraciflua
TULIP TREE ....Liriodendron tulipifera
FLOWERING CRAB APPLES ....Malus varieties
BLACK TUPELO...................Nyssa sylvatica
SORREL TREE ....Oxydendrum arboreum
AMERICAN SYCAMORE............Platanus occidentalis
THUNDERCLOUD PLUM ....Prunus cerasifera 'Thundercloud'
SARGENT CHERRY................Prunus sargenti
DOUGLAS FIR....................Pseudotsuga taxifolia (Rocky Mt. Strains)
WHITE OAK ....Quercus alba
RED OAK........................Quercus borealis
SCARLET OAK ....Quercus coccinea
PIN OAK........................Quercus palustris
THURLOW WEEPING WILLOW .....Salix elegantissima
CORKSCREW WILLOW.............Salix matsudana tortuosa
JAPANESE PAGODA TREE ....Sophora japonica
REGENT PAGODA TREE ....Sophora japonica 'Regent'
JAPANESE TREE LILAC...........Syringa amurensis japonica
SILVER LINDEN..................Tilia tomentosa
CHRISTINE BUISMAN ELM.........Ulmus carpinifolia 'Christine Buisman'

113

Trees for the temperate middle zone

Zones 5 and 6 are the northern limits of hardiness for a great variety of ornamental and shade trees. The lists which follow do not, of course, suggest that these are the only trees for these areas. Many trees found in previous lists, European Beech and Flowering Dogwood, for example, also thrive in Zones 5 and 6. Remember, too, that hardiness is also modified by many climatic factors. Mere temperature gradients are not the whole story. Yearly totals and monthly distribution of rainfall are of equal importance. The Japanese Dogwood, which is perfectly at home in well-watered Zone 5 portions of Pennsylvania, will languish in areas of New Mexico with similar temperature limits but great aridity.

Much work still lies ahead in exploring the full limits of hardiness. European foresters have very carefully worked out the precise adaptability of dozens of geographical races of Norway Spruce and Scotch Pine. They know exactly which ones are best for any area. But horticulturists have been exceedingly lax about investigating races and hardiness among ornamental and shade trees. All too often seed from any handy source is planted without regard to its merits. The parent stock of a species introduced into this country is often by no means the best or hardiest strain available. By more diligent plant exploration, thoughtful introduction, and careful testing here in North America, the limits of hardiness of many trees discussed in this book can surely be extended considerably to the north.

The following list covers trees which are at present known to be hardy in Zones 5 and 6. They are listed alphabetically by botanical name. Those species which are also excellent for planting in gardens in warmer regions are marked with an asterisk(*).

BLUE ATLAS CEDAR, Cedrus atlantica glauca

JAPANESE DOGWOOD, Cornus kousa

114

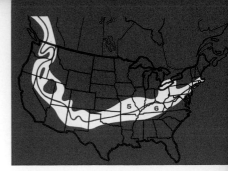

TREES HARDY IN ZONE 5
(Winter temperatures dropping to from —5° to —10° F.)

*JAPANESE MAPLE . . . . .Acer palmatum varieties
 SYCAMORE MAPLE . . . . .Acer pseudoplatanus
 HARDY SILK TREE. . . . . .Albizzia julibrissin rosea
*CHINESE CHESTNUT . . . . .Castanea mollissima
*BLUE ATLAS CEDAR . . . . .Cedrus atlantica glauca
*WHITEBUD . . . . .Cercis canadensis alba
*WITHER'S PINK REDBUD . . . . . . .Cercis canadensis 'Wither's Pink Charm'
*PINK DOGWOOD . . . . .Cornus florida rubra
 JAPANESE DOGWOOD. . . . . .Cornus kousa
*MODESTO ASH. . . . . .Fraxinus velutina 'Modesto'
*AMERICAN HOLLY . . . . .Ilex opaca
*GOLDEN-RAIN TREE. . . . . .Koelreuteria paniculata
 VOSSI LABURNUM . . . . .Laburnum vossi
 YULAN MAGNOLIA . . . . .Magnolia denudata
*SAUCER MAGNOLIA . . . . .Magnolia soulangeana varieties
 STAR MAGNOLIA . . . . .Magnolia stellata
*SWEET BAY . . . . .Magnolia virginiana
 SARGENT CRAB APPLE. . . . . .Malus sargenti
*DAWN REDWOOD. . . . . .Metasequoia glyptostroboides
 LONDON PLANE TREE . . . . .Platanus acerifolia
*HARDY ORANGE . . . . .Poncirus trifoliata
 BLIREIANA PLUM . . . . .Prunus blireiana
 PEACH . . . . .Prunus persica
*KWANZAN CHERRY. . . . . .Prunus serrulata 'Kwanzan'
*AUTUMN CHERRY . . . . .Prunus subhirtella autumnalis
*WEEPING HIGAN CHERRY. . . . . .Prunus subhirtella pendula
*YOSHINO CHERRY. . . . . .Prunus yedoensis
*BRADFORD CALLERY PEAR . . . . .Pyrus calleryana 'Bradford'
 COMMON PEAR. . . . . .Pyrus communis
*WILLOW OAK . . . . .Quercus phellos
 KOREAN MOUNTAIN-ASH . . . . . .Sorbus alnifolia
*JAPANESE STEWARTIA. . . . . .Stewartia pseudocamellia
*JAPANESE SNOWBELL. . . . . .Styrax japonica
 CRIMEAN LINDEN . . . . .Tilia euchlora
*CHINESE ELM . . . . .Ulmus parvifolia
 JAPANESE ZELKOVA . . . . .Zelkova serrata
*VILLAGE GREEN ZELKOVA . . . . .Zelkova serrata 'Village Green'

TREES HARDY IN ZONE 6
(Winter temperatures dropping to from —5° to 5° F.)

*SILK TREE . . . . .Albizzia julibrissin varieties
*ATLAS CEDAR. . . . . .Cedrus atlantica
 ENGLISH HOLLY. . . . . .Ilex aquifolium
*AMANOGAWA CHERRY . . . . .Prunus serrulata 'Amanogawa'
*SHIROFUGEN CHERRY . . . . .Prunus serrulata 'Shiro-fugen'
*MOUNT FUJI CHERRY. . . . . .Prunus serrulata 'Shirotae'
*BABYLON WEEPING WILLOW. . . .Salix babylonica

Trees for the Mid-south

Although some beautiful Northerners like the mountain-ashes, horse-chestnuts, hemlocks, and birches are not suitable for southern gardens, their places are taken by other trees which will tolerate heat and are not hardy in the North. The trees listed below are excellent varieties for the Mid-south. They are listed in alphabetical order by their botanical names. These lists are not meant to exclude many trees hardy in Zones 5 or 6 and also excellent choices for planting in southern gardens. (See page 115)

TREES HARDY IN ZONE 7
(Winter temperatures dropping to from 5° to 10° F.)

DEODAR CEDAR . . . .**Cedrus deodara**
PACIFIC DOGWOOD . . . .**Cornus nuttalli** (West Coast only)
LOQUAT . . . .**Eriobotrya japonica**
TOYON . . . .**Heteromeles arbutifolia**
CRAPE-MYRTLE . . . .**Lagerstroemia indica varieties**
GLOSSY PRIVET. . . . .**Ligustrum lucidum**
SOUTHERN MAGNOLIA . . . .**Magnolia grandiflora**
CHINESE PHOTINIA . . . .**Photinia serrulata**
LIVE OAK . . . .**Quercus virginiana**
STRAWBERRY TREE. . . . .**Arbutus unedo**

TREES HARDY IN ZONE 8
(Winter temperatures dropping to from 10° to 20° F.)

CANARY PINE . . . .**Pinus canariensis**
CHINESE WINDMILL PALM . . . .**Trachycarpus fortunei**

WASHINGTON FAN PALM, Washingtonia filifera

EVERGLADE PALM, Paurotis wrighti

Trees for the Deep South

In the loose term, the Deep South, are included areas in which winter frosts are mild and of short duration. Many trees like southern magnolias, live oaks, and crape-myrtles which are hardy further north are also excellent choices for planting in the Deep South. The following species are perfectly at home in hot and virtually frost-free climates.

TREES HARDY IN ZONE 9

(Winter temperatures dropping to from 20° to 30° F.)

SILVER WATTLE............................**Acacia decurrens dealbata**

SOUTH AMERICAN JELLY PALM............**Butia capitata**

CAMPHOR TREE...........................**Cinnamomum camphora**

CITRUS FRUITS.............................**Citrus species**

CRIMSON EUCALYPTUS....................**Eucalyptus ficifolia**

TASMANIAN BLUE EUCALYPTUS..........**Eucalyptus globulus**

COMMON OLIVE..........................**Olea europaea**

CHINESE PISTACHE.......................**Pistacia chinensis**

CALIFORNIA LIVE OAK...................**Quercus agrifolia**

BRAZILIAN PEPPER TREE.................**Schinus terebinthifolius**

TREES HARDY IN ZONE 10

(Winter temperatures dropping to from 30° to 40° F.)

COOTAMUNDRA WATTLE.................**Acacia baileyana**

ORCHID TREE.............................**Bauhinia variegata**

SHOWER-OF-GOLD.......................**Cassia fistula**

CAROB...................................**Ceratonia siliqua**

COCONUT................................**Cocos nucifera**

MORETON BAY FIG........................**Ficus macrophylla**

INDIAN LAUREL FIG......................**Ficus retusa**

SHARPLEAF JACARANDA.................**Jacaranda acutifolia**

EVERGLADE PALM.......................**Paurotis wrighti**

CANARY ISLAND DATE PALM.............**Phoenix canariensis**

SENEGAL DATE PALM....................**Phoenix reclinata**

ROYAL PALM.............................**Roystonea regia**

WASHINGTON FAN PALM.................**Washingtonia filifera**

MEXICAN FAN PALM.....................**Washingtonia robusta**

Trees for city planting

The down-town city environment is one of the most difficult of all for trees. It is worse, in fact, than desert areas, because if water can be supplied in the desert, many trees will grow there with great vigor.

In its final effect on trees, city soil has much in common with desert soil. It is normally exceedingly dry because most of the soil surface is covered with paving that is almost impervious to rain water. In many northern cities, heating pipes run beneath the sidewalks to melt the winter snow. This further dries out the soil even in winter time. Where there are no heating pipes, salt compounds are commonly spread on paved areas to melt snow. The brine that runs into tree root zones produces soils of high salinity.

City soil itself has usually been re-worked so many times that it is often little more than an aggregate of brickbats, clay and rubble. Trees growing on city streets must contend not only with impoverished dry soil, but also with intense summer heat, greatly multiplied by reflection from building walls and pavement.

To cap it all, city air is highly polluted with a disturbing variety of toxic gasses which cause the rapid defoliation of all but a few highly resistant species. Small wonder that the list of trees which will grow in the city is an exceedingly short one.

Soil preparation for planting city trees is obviously a major problem. It must be done well and thoroughly. In most cases, the earth removed from the planting pit or hole should simply be discarded, hauled away and completely replaced with the best grade of fertile, friable top soil, in which the tree is planted. Remember that, living under difficult conditions at best, the tree will have to depend on this new soil for almost all of its future growth. In effect, it will be growing in a sunken window box or container.

Organic materials cannot be used for mulching after planting. They will soon be tramped flat, blown away, or destroyed by fire from carelessly dropped cigarettes. The best solution is to cover the entire surface of the planting pit with a metal grill. Such a protective device will prevent the constant tramp of pedestrian traffic from pounding the soil into a mass so hard that neither water nor life-giving oxygen can penetrate it. In some cities a layer of coarse gravel is placed below the metal grill as a further safeguard against soil compaction. In residential or apartment house areas, a two foot cylindrical metal guard around the trunk will be necessary to ward off the constant attentions of city dogs.

If it can be arranged so that the pavement rises slightly to the edge of the planting pit and metal grill, the worst effects of pavement salting can be avoided. The snow brine will run down the gutters rather than into the tree's root area. Trees that are to be given special attention are often planted with a small water pipe beneath the pavement connecting the nearest water supply to the planting pit. This greatly facilitates the ease and safety of summer watering.

In city gardens, the problems of soil compaction are not as severe as they are on streetside locations. However, unless the tree is growing in a small area of lawn or ground cover plants, a grill or paving stones laid on coarse gravel should cover any part of the root area likely to be subjected to regular traffic. Here too, more careful attention will have to be paid to proper watering and fertilizing than is necessary in a suburban or country yard.

The following list of trees have proven themselves to be the best for planting in city locations. Those marked with an asterisk (*) are especially tolerant of polluted city air.

118

TREES FOR CITY PLANTING

Common Name	Botanical Name	Northern Limit of Hardiness Zone
SUMMERSHADE MAPLE	Acer platanoides 'Summershade'	3
SILK TREE	Albizzia julibrissin	6
DOWNY HAWTHORN	Crataegus mollis	4
WASHINGTON HAWTHORN	Crataegus phaenopyrum	4
RUSSIAN OLIVE	Elaeagnus angustifolia	2
MARSHALL'S SEEDLESS ASH	Fraxinus pennsylvanica 'Marshall's Seedless'	2
GINKGO	Ginkgo biloba	4
*THORNLESS HONEY-LOCUST VARIETIES	Gleditsia triacanthos inermis varieties	4
GOLDEN-RAIN TREE	Koelreuteria paniculata	5
GLOSSY PRIVET	Ligustrum lucidum	7
SOUTHERN MAGNOLIA	Magnolia grandiflora	7
SAUCER MAGNOLIA	Magnolia soulangeana	5
STAR MAGNOLIA	Magnolia stellata	5
*AMUR CORK TREE	Phellodendron amurense	3
*LONDON PLANE TREE	Platanus acerifolia	5
HARDY ORANGE	Poncirus trifoliata	5
BRADFORD CALLERY PEAR	Pyrus calleryana 'Bradford'	5
*REGENT SCHOLAR TREE	Sophora japonica 'Regent'	4
*GREENSPIRE LINDEN	Tilia cordata 'Greenspire'	3
CRIMEAN LINDEN	Tilia euchlora	5
SILVER LINDEN	Tilia tomentosa	4
VILLAGE GREEN ZELKOVA	Zelkova serrata 'Village Green'	5

Trees for seashore planting

Seaside conditions impose special hardships on plant life. These increase as the proximity to the ocean increases until at the high water mark itself only a few very highly specialized plants can exist. These adverse factors include varying degrees of salinity in the soil, frequent and severe winds often drenched with salt spray, and the sandy soils of many coastal areas, poor in water holding capacity and in minerals essential for tree growth. It is difficult to generalize about coastal conditions and the trees which will grow there because they are not uniform. Besides obvious variations in coastal climate and temperature, the quality of coastal soils also differs. The soil on much of the coast of Maine for example is basically an inland soil on which the sea has gradually encroached. The soil on the coast of southern New Jersey in contrast is a fine-grained sandy type which was formerly the floor of a shallow sea. Consequently, although trees for either location must be species which will withstand wind and salt spray, the more fertile Maine soil will permit a greater latitude of selection than the New Jersey sands which are deficient in mineral nutrients.

Good soil preparation prior to planting is especially important in establishing trees in seashore locations, particularly in sandy areas. Abundant humus, 50 per cent by volume, should be mixed with the soil in which the trees are planted. This helps retain moisture about the roots in rapidly drying sandy soils until the tree can put forth the wide-ranging root system necessary to sustain its growth. A thick but porous mulch is also of great value in retaining moisture around the tree.

The following list covers a group of trees which have been found to withstand coastal conditions and salt spray. Those marked with an asterisk (*) have proven to be especially well adapted to proximity to salt water.

SHADBLOW SERVICEBERRY, Amelanchier canadensis

EUCALYPTUS

120

TREES FOR SEASHORE PLANTING

Common Name	Botanical Name	Northern Limit of Hardiness Zone
NORWAY MAPLE	Acer platanoides	3
*SYCAMORE MAPLE	Acer pseudoplatanus	5
*SHADBLOW SERVICEBERRY	Amelanchier canadensis	4
SOUTH AMERICAN JELLY PALM	Butia capitata	9
*COCONUT	Cocus nucifera	10
WASHINGTON HAWTHORN	Crataegus phaenopyrum	4
ENGLISH HAWTHORN	Crataegus oxyacantha	4
*RUSSIAN OLIVE	Elaeagnus angustifolia	2
EUCALYPTUS	Eucalyptus species	9
THORNLESS HONEYLOCUST	Gleditsia triacanthos inermis varieties	4
AMERICAN HOLLY	Ilex opaca	5
*EASTERN RED CEDAR	Juniperus virginiana	2
SOUTHERN MAGNOLIA	Magnolia grandiflora	7
*BLACK TUPELO	Nyssa sylvatica	4
*COMMON OLIVE	Olea europaea	9
*LONDON PLANE TREE	Platanus acerifolia	5
*HARDY ORANGE	Poncirus trifoliata	5
CALIFORNIA LIVE OAK	Quercus agrifolia	9
*LIVE OAK	Quercus virginiana	7
ROYAL PALM	Roystonea regia	10
GOLDEN WEEPING WILLOW	Salix alba tristis	2
BRAZILIAN PEPPER TREE	Schinus terebinthifolius	9
JAPANESE PAGODA TREE	Sophora japonica	4
DARK AMERICAN ARBORVITAE	Thuja occidentalis nigra	2
CRIMEAN LINDEN	Tilia euchlora	5
*CHINESE WINDMILL PALM	Trachycarpus fortunei	8
CHINESE ELM	Ulmus parvifolia	5
MEXICAN FAN PALM	Washingtonia robusta	10

Trees for arid locations

One of the most interesting demonstrations of the variability of trees and their different water requirements is encountered as one drives west across the central part of the United States. The trip starts in the high-rainfall areas of the East where there is great diversity of tree life. Then gradually, as one progresses, species after species drops out until only a tough minority is left. Finally, as one approaches the well-watered areas of the Pacific Coast, the process reverses itself and a greater variety again appears.

The need for drouth-tolerant trees is not entirely confined to naturally dry areas. They are also desirable even in areas where there is considerable natural rainfall if the soil is extremely sandy and water quickly disappears.

It is, of course, possible to grow trees other than the desert species in very dry areas if they are regularly watered. But it is certainly safer and wiser to plant highly drouth-tolerant species even if abundant water is available.

The following list of trees includes those well adapted to arid locations. The zone of hardiness for each tree is given. This is important since some will grow only in subtropical areas. Those species tolerant of very alkaline soils are marked with an asterisk (*).

The trees are listed in alphabetical order according to their botanical names.

Species	Botanical Name	Zone of Hardiness
*COOTAMUNDRA WATTLE	Acacia baileyana	10
*SILVER WATTLE	Acacia decurrens dealbata	9
SILK TREE	Albizzia julibrissin	6
*ORCHID TREE	Bauhinia variegata	10
SOUTH AMERICAN JELLY PALM	Butia capitata	9
*CAROB	Ceratonia siliqua	10
*RUSSIAN OLIVE	Eleagnus angustifolia	2
*EUCALYPTUS	Eucalyptus species	9
MARSHALL'S SEEDLESS ASH	Fraxinus pennsylvanica 'Marshall's Seedless'	2
*MODESTO ASH	Fraxinus velutina 'Modesto'	5
HONEY LOCUST	Gleditsia triacanthos varieties	4
*WESTERN RED-CEDAR	Juniperus scopulorum	4
*EASTERN RED-CEDAR	Juniperus virginiana	2
*GOLDEN-RAIN TREE	Koelreuteria paniculata	5
COMMON OLIVE	Olea europaea	9
CANARY PINE	Pinus canariensis	8
CHINESE PISTACHE	Pistacia chinensis	9
*BRAZILIAN PEPPER TREE	Schinus terebinthifolius	9
CHINESE ELM	Ulmus parvifolia	5
*WASHINGTON FAN PALM	Washingtonia filifera	10
*MEXICAN FAN PALM	Washingtonia robusta	10

Trees requiring acid soil

Most trees grow satisfactorily in a considerable range of soils either on the acid or on the alkaline side of neutral, although more species will grow in mildly acid than in alkaline soils. A few trees must have acid soil in order to survive. This phenomenon is related to their need for iron and other minor elements. Iron is almost inactivated in alkaline soils, and its absence causes the foliage of some trees that are normally green to turn a pale yellow color. If the condition is very severe, the foliage may turn brown and the tree may even die. This yellow-leaf condition, called chlorosis, can be corrected by acidifying the soil with sulfur, or by spraying the young foliage with an organic iron compound. However, if the soil is definitely and positively alkaline, even these treatments are only temporarily effective. The chlorosis will reappear in time.

The following list includes trees which must have acid soil (pH 6.5 or under) for satisfactory growth. Those marked with an asterisk (*) are especially dependent upon acid soil conditions for survival. They are listed in alphabetical order by their botanical names.

JAPANESE MAPLE	Acer palmatum varieties
*STRAWBERRY TREE	Arbutus unedo
*CITRUS FRUITS	Citrus species
FLOWERING DOGWOOD	Cornus florida varieties
JAPANESE DOGWOOD	Cornus kousa
PACIFIC DOGWOOD	Cornus nuttalli
EUROPEAN BEECH	Fagus sylvatica varieties
*ENGLISH HOLLY	Ilex aquifolium
*AMERICAN HOLLY	Ilex opaca
SWEET BAY	Magnolia virginiana
BLACK TUPELO	Nyssa sylvatica
*SORREL TREE	Oxydendrum arboreum
HARDY ORANGE	Poncirus trifoliata
RED OAK	Quercus borealis
*SCARLET OAK	Quercus coccinea
*PIN OAK	Quercus palustris
*WILLOW OAK	Quercus phellos
JAPANESE STEWARTIA	Stewartia pseudocamellia

Espaliered trees

The training of fruit trees in geometrical shapes is an ancient and fascinating art long practiced in Europe, but almost unknown in this country. Espaliered trees are usually trained flat against the sunny walls of buildings or grown low to form attractive fences around flower or vegetable gardens. This special method of growing has advantages in fruit production. The trees are kept artificially small, which greatly facilitates spraying, thinning, and picking the fruit. The dwarfing effect of the rigorous pruning greatly hastens the aging of the tree and causes it to bear earlier than it normally would if grown untrimmed. The shelter and protection of a sunny wall makes it possible to grow tender fruit trees farther north than their normal limit of hardiness in the field. Thus peaches and apricots, for example, can be grown and fruited as espaliers much farther north than in commercial peach orchards. Fruit trees grafted on dwarfing root stocks are especially well adapted to espalier training because their growth is greatly limited by the effect of the special understock used. This means that much less yearly pruning is needed to keep the espalier in bounds and in the proper shape. The dwarfing understock also greatly advances the bearing age of the tree and even three- or four-year-old trees will bear fine fruit of normal size and color, contrary to what one might expect.

The espaliering of ornamental and flowering trees is on the increase at present. This growth in popularity is due in large part to changes in domestic architectural design. Instead of the regularly placed windows of traditional architectural styles, many modern houses have large wall areas of wood or masonry unbroken by fenestration. Such a blank wall is a perfect foil for the display of an espaliered tree, which greatly increases its beauty and interest by the pattern of branching, foliage textures, play of light and shadow, and colorful blooms which

the tree can provide. Ornamental tree espaliers are usually not trained in geometrical shapes but are made by attaching and spreading out the branches in a simple fan shape, flat against the wall (See opposite page.) One of the outstanding collections of espaliered ornamental trees in the world is to be found on the campus of Princeton University in Princeton, New Jersey. A remarkable assortment of magnolias, flowering plums, sorrel trees, tamarisks, and many other trees and shrubs have been grown and maintained for years on the walls of magnificent stone buildings. This feature alone, quite aside from the exceptionally complete collection of shade and flowering trees on the rest of the campus, draws thousands of visitors to the university each year.

All that is required for this fascinating horticultural art is a suitable wall, (prepared by stretching a series of wires between bolts or lag screws in the wall) garden shears, and patience. An easy way to prepare a wall for this purpose is to attach to it a section of the rectangular-mesh woven-wire galvanized fencing used for enclosing cattle or horse pastures. This fencing comes in 4 or 5 foot widths and the cross wires are already firmly woven in place. It lasts for years without painting. The small tree to be trained is planted as close to the wall as possible and the branches are gently bent into the pattern desired and tied in place with strips of cloth, soft rope or the wide plastic-covered wire "twist-ems".

The accompanying illustrations show the steps followed in creating a simple four-branched espalier from a young two year old tree (A) as it is received from the nursery. The branches are bent over gently and tied to two parallel wires in a horizontal position as shown in figure B. The tree then grows many upright shoots as shown in figure C. The following spring, the best placed upright shoots are tied to four vertical wires as shown in figure

ESPALIER TRAINING FOR ORNAMENTAL TREES

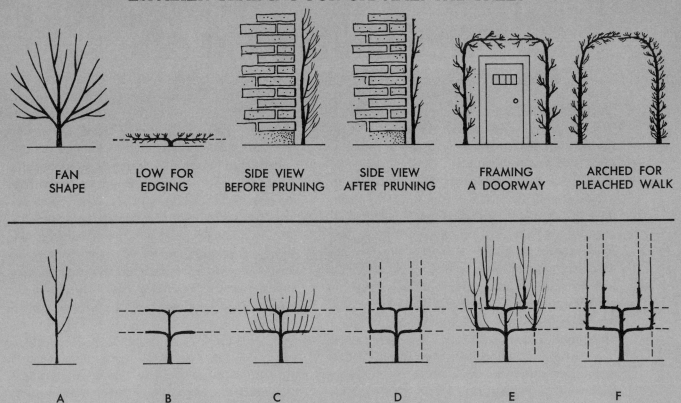

FAN SHAPE   LOW FOR EDGING   SIDE VIEW BEFORE PRUNING   SIDE VIEW AFTER PRUNING   FRAMING A DOORWAY   ARCHED FOR PLEACHED WALK

A   B   C   D   E   F

D. All surplus shoots are cut off at their points of origin on the horizontal branches. The tree grows a new crop of shoots during the following summer as shown in figure E. The next spring all shoots are cut back to short two inch spurs except for one at the end of each upright shoot, which is retained to elongate the uprights as shown in figure F. From this point on, the main branches of the tree have been established and subsequent shoots are cut back to spurs each spring. This repeated trimming encourages the tree to produce short spurs of blooming wood on which flowers and fruit are borne.

The other illustrations show some of the infinite variety of espaliered trees which can be created to serve various decorative and useful purposes. The fan shaped form is one used to form wall patterns of many ornamental trees such as magnolias, flowering crab apples, flowering cherries and other small growing trees. The low two-branched espalier is extensively used in Europe as a decorative enclosure for garden plots. A row of arched espaliers trained to intertwine with each other is used to make a pleached allée or a little summer house in the garden. The wall drawing shows how espaliered trees are trimmed each year or two to keep the desired flat shape against a wall.

Espaliered trees require care in shaping and maintenance, but no more care than a properly maintained rose garden. They offer a wonderful opportunity for creative gardening and illustrate the remarkable plasticity of woody plant material in the hands of an imaginative gardener.

Tree planting and care

Where to plant

As a general rule, the easiest time to plant a tree is in the early spring, just before the buds open and new growth begins. The advantage in planting at this time is that the tree is still in a safe resting condition but is ready to begin the surge of new root and branch growth which it makes each year at this time. There is normally abundant moisture in the soil after the winter rains and snows and frequent watering is unnecessary. Spring transplanting is especially favorable for broadleaf evergreen trees which retain their foliage in winter and would be injured by drying winter winds if moved in the fall. It is also best for varieties like magnolias and tulip trees whose fleshy roots are easily injured and slow to regenerate. Coniferous evergreen trees also transplant with ease in the spring.

The next best time to transplant trees is in the fall after the leaves have ripened and dropped off, but before the ground freezes up. Not all trees move safely in the fall, notable examples being evergreens, plums, magnolias and Red and Silver Maples, especially in northerly sections of the country where the ground is frozen hard and deeply during the winter. But for most trees, the advantages of fall planting are that the ground settles well around the roots during the winter rains, and all of the new spring root growth (which begins before bud break is evident) takes place in the now location where it will do the most good. If spring planting must be long delayed by repeated rains as is sometimes the case, trees moved the fall previously can start growth in a normal fashion and benefit from the added moisture.

If trees are dug with a ball of the earth in which they were previously growing still intact around the roots, they can also be safely transplanted in the winter or the summer months. In the latter case, extra care and hardening up is necessary and it takes a knowledgable professional nurseryman to do it properly. The ball should be partially dug, in the form of a circular trench with the ball forming the inside wall. The trench is filled with water which soaks in and moistens the ball, giving the tree an extra heavy drink. Then the tree is dug completely and moved, often after a period

HOW TREES ARE SOLD

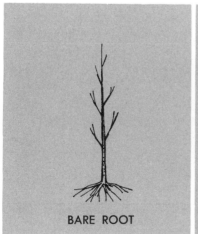

BARE ROOT

BALLED AND BURLAPPED

CONTAINER GROWN

of storage in a cool shady location to harden up the foliage and new shoots. The foliage is often sprayed with an anti-dessicant material, but this is not really necessary if the tree is properly hardened, and there is still some basic research to be done before the role of anti-dessicants is fully understood and their application perfected.

Trees which have been previously grown in large containers, and are in effect large scale pot plants, can of course be successfully planted at any time of the year. If they are planted in the hot summer months, careful watering will be necessary to prevent excessive drying until the roots have grown out into the earth in their new location. All things considered, early spring is still the easiest time to plant a tree, especially if the home owner is doing his own planting.

How trees are moved

When a tree is dug from the location in which it has been growing and moved to a new one, it leaves in its former location part of the root system which nourished it and provided needed water. It is therefore in a unnatural condition until such time as the roots have grown into the soil of their new home and normal top growth is resumed. The basic principle in all transplanting therefore is to prevent drying out of the roots and top of the tree during this critical period. The three most important principles in tree transplanting are keeping the roots and top moist during the shipping and planting time, proper pruning to reduce the size of the top, and watering after replanting at intervals frequent enough to keep the soil moist but not soggy.

Trees are supplied by nurseries in three different ways depending on how easily the variety can be transplanted and also upon the climate of the area where the transplanting is done. Varieties like small crab apples and the smaller sizes of maples, for example, which are easy to move are often sold "bare root" with

the roots free from earth but protected by moist packing material. Varieties such as magnolias which are more difficult to move and the larger sizes of most trees are usually moved "balled and burlapped". In this method the roots remain undisturbed in a ball of the soil in which they were growing in the nursery, and the ball of earth is secured by a burlap covering and tightly wrapped with strong rope. In arid sections of the country, trees are frequently grown in containers, in which case all of the roots of the tree are intact and undamaged within the container. Container-grown trees are also frequently sold in humid sections of the country, since they can be transplanted safely at any time of the year, so long as they are watered sufficiently until they become established in their new location.

Planting the tree

If the tree has been received "bare root" from the supplier, the roots should be thoroughly soaked prior to planting. Small trees can be stood in a tub of water while the planting pit is dug. The planting pit or hole should be dug 6 inches wider than the root spread of the tree and usually about 18 inches deep. Trees should never be forced or twisted into holes too small for the roots, as this is a primary reason for the "girdling roots" which can later cause the mysterious decline of a fine shade tree.

Place the tree in the hole at the same depth at which it grew in the nursery as indicated by the clearly visible soil line at the base of the trunk. Shovel in around the roots a mixture of 1/3 peat or humus and 2/3 soil excavated from the pit. Chemical fertilizer should not be mixed with the soil because it is so easy to add too much and "burn" the roots. Shake the tree occasionally during the filling process to work the fine soil in thoroughly around the roots. After the tree is planted, tramp the soil in firmly but do not pound it hard. With the remainder of the soil, form a little saucer-like

BARE ROOT PLANTING

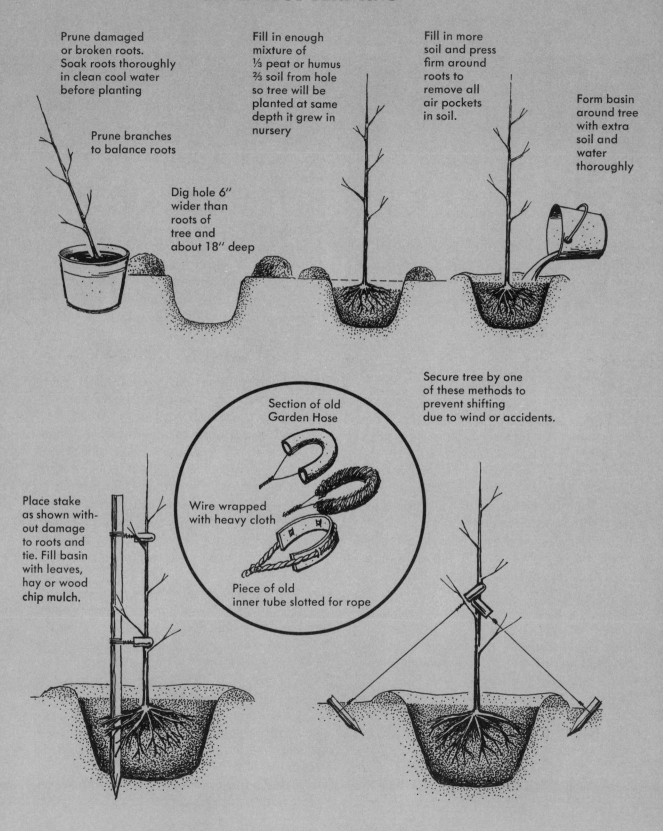

Prune damaged or broken roots. Soak roots thoroughly in clean cool water before planting

Prune branches to balance roots

Dig hole 6" wider than roots of tree and about 18" deep

Fill in enough mixture of ⅓ peat or humus ⅔ soil from hole so tree will be planted at same depth it grew in nursery

Fill in more soil and press firm around roots to remove all air pockets in soil.

Form basin around tree with extra soil and water thoroughly

Secure tree by one of these methods to prevent shifting due to wind or accidents.

Place stake as shown without damage to roots and tie. Fill basin with leaves, hay or wood chip mulch.

Section of old Garden Hose

Wire wrapped with heavy cloth

Piece of old inner tube slotted for rope

BALLED IN BURLAP

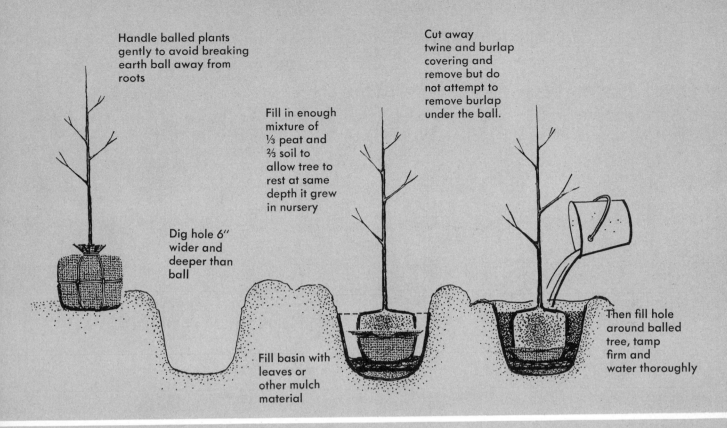

Handle balled plants gently to avoid breaking earth ball away from roots

Dig hole 6" wider and deeper than ball

Fill in enough mixture of ⅓ peat and ⅔ soil to allow tree to rest at same depth it grew in nursery

Fill basin with leaves or other mulch material

Cut away twine and burlap covering and remove but do not attempt to remove burlap under the ball.

Then fill hole around balled tree, tamp firm and water thoroughly

CONTAINER GROWN TREES

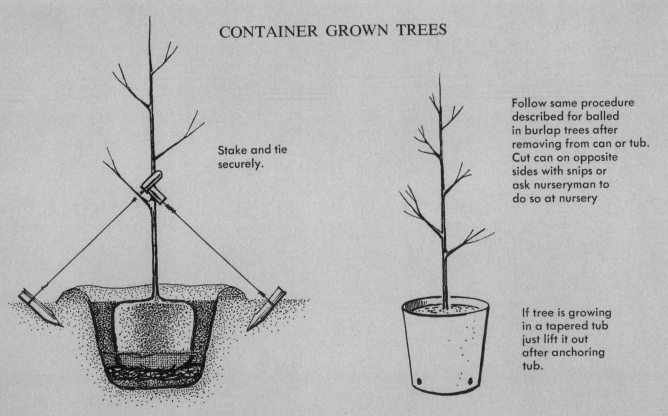

Stake and tie securely.

Follow same procedure described for balled in burlap trees after removing from can or tub. Cut can on opposite sides with snips or ask nurseryman to do so at nursery

If tree is growing in a tapered tub just lift it out after anchoring tub.

PRUNING A TREE FOR TRANSPLANTING

Before
Pruning

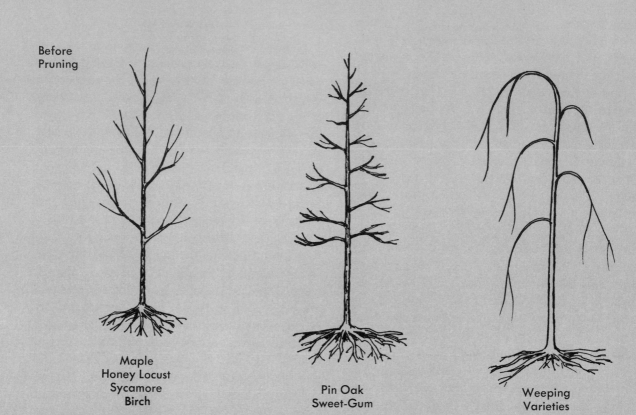

Maple
Honey Locust
Sycamore
Birch

Pin Oak
Sweet-Gum

Weeping
Varieties

After
Pruning

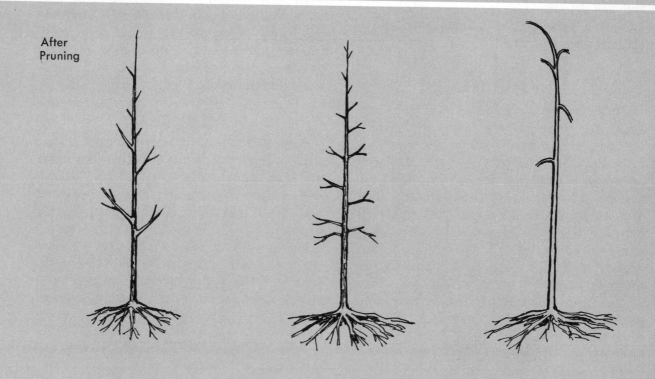

ridge around the outside of the pit. Water thoroughly and fill the saucer completely with leaves, salt hay, wood chips, or some similar mulching material to conserve moisture.

If a balled and burlapped tree is being planted, a similar process is followed except that the hole is first back-filled with soil-humus mix high enough so that the tree in its ball sits at the same level it occupied in the nursery. Then the ropes and burlap are cut away from the top and sides of the ball and removed. Do not attempt to remove the burlap under the ball or this may break it. The hole is then filled in around the ball with soil mix, tamping it firmly but not shaking the tree, and the outer rim or saucer is formed and treated as above. Large balled trees are usually too heavy to be handled by an individual and are best planted by a nurseryman with an experienced crew and proper equipment.

Container grown trees, if small, can be inverted and removed from the container by tapping it repeatedly. Large container grown trees are best set at the proper level in the hole and then the sides of the container are cut away and removed. Back-filling proceeds as outlined above.

Pruning

To insure rapid vigorous growth in its new home, the branches of a newly transplanted tree should be pruned back so that there is a favorable balance of root over top. Damaged or broken branches should be trimmed off below the point of injury. The central "leader" or trunk should be left intact to build a high crown and the side branches should be shortened in by at least ½ their length. (See illustrations.) This seems harsh treatment, but the rapid re-growth which results more than justifies it. More trees are lost by neglecting proper pruning than any other cause. Broken roots should be cut off above the break and bruised ends cut off cleanly as they will regenerate much more rapidly.

Staking

Newly planted trees benefit from the support of a strong stake to prevent loosening by the wind, or playing children, until the roots have grown fast in their new location. A strong 1½ or 2 inch thick stake should be driven into the ground about 6 inches from the trunk. A piece of pliant wire can be threaded through an 8 or 10 inch section of used rubber hose or thickly wound with cloth. The wire is formed in a figure 8 with the trunk of the tree in the covered portion and the wire securely wrapped around the stake. The stake in position should be 2/3 the height of the tree with the top wire high enough to give good support. Large trees, 2½ inches in diameter or more, are often too big to stake and are secured by guying the tree with 3 heavy wires stretching from above the lower limbs to stakes driven into the ground 3 or 4 feet from the base of the tree. The portion of the wire which goes around the trunk should be protected by a section of hose or thick cloth wrapping on the wire loop. Such wires should not be left in place after the second growing season or they will cut into the trunk. Wrapping the trunk of a newly transplanted tree with a spiral strip of burlap or heavy creped paper tree wrap will reduce water loss and enhance subsequent growth.

After care

Even well mulched trees will benefit from a weekly thorough soaking if the weather turns dry after transplanting time. Fill the "saucer" to the brim with water and let it soak in. After new growth has taken place, a good soaking with liquid fertilizer diluted according to the manufacturer's directions will pay big dividends in health and vigor. If leaf-chewing insects or aphids appear, the state or provincial entomologist or extension specialist in insect pests can provide up-to-date information on the best sprays to use. A reliable local nurseryman is a valuable source of information on tree care in his area.

Care in later years

Fertilizing

If a newly planted tree is set in an area with fertile soil, it will need little additional fertilizer to develop normally. However, many new homes are located on lots which have been bulldozed and regraded. Often the original top soil is diluted, buried, or sometimes even removed entirely and sold elsewhere. Trees grow much more rapidly and have better health in such areas if a regular fertilizing schedule is followed. A good grade of commercial fertilizer (10-6-4 or 8-8-8-analyses are both good) should be applied early each spring at the rate of 1 lb. of fertilizer for each inch of tree trunk diameter at breast height. The fertilizer should be applied evenly within a circle as wide as the spread of the branches and lightly scratched in with a rake or garden cultivator. If a heavy sod of grass is growing under the tree, holes can be punched or drilled at 1 foot intervals in the circle beneath the branches and the fertilizer distributed in these holes. Sod should not be allowed to grow up to the trunk of newly planted trees. Instead a circle 2 or 3 feet in diameter should be kept free of vegetation and mulched for the first two years of the tree's growth, which will be much more rapid if it does not have to compete with grass for fertilizer and moisture.

If tree growing in lawn, punch or drill holes 1 foot apart around the tree and apply fertilizer. Do not permit grass to grow up to trunk of young trees.

Pruning

Trees which are properly pruned at planting time will require little more attention for several years. From then on, lower branches may be gradually removed if a higher head or crown is desired. Crossed branches which rub against each other should have one of them removed or if a branch rubs against the trunk, the branch should be removed. If the trunk forks equally in a long narrow "V" crotch, one of the forks should be shortened, especially in areas subject to ice storms. A "V" crotch is a point of structural weakness and will split if the branches become loaded with ice, or occasionally in a wind storm when the foliage is wet and heavy. Espaliered trees grown flat on walls require yearly pruning to preserve their shape and limit their size. Fruit trees are pruned severely in the top of the crown to limit their height and build a wide spreading but low head of branches. Such branches are easy to spray and pick when the fruit ripens, and this form of head permits the sunlight to penetrate the crown and color and ripen the fruit uniformly.

When branches are snapped by ice or wind storms, they should be cleanly cut off below the point of damage. The broken branch should first be cut off at the break to remove its weight and then a second clean cut made below the fractured area. Even if no side branchlets are visible at the time of the cut, deciduous trees will regenerate new branches from bark buds to replace the lost branch area. Snapped branches of coniferous trees usually do not form these adventitious buds and should be neatly cut off where the branch joins the trunk. When branches of any tree are removed for one reason or another, the branch should first be sawed off a couple of feet from the trunk and then the stub should be removed by cutting it off flush with the trunk. This flush cut permits

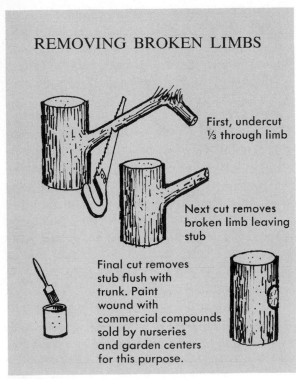

REMOVING BROKEN LIMBS

First, undercut ⅓ through limb

Next cut removes broken limb leaving stub

Final cut removes stub flush with trunk. Paint wound with commercial compounds sold by nurseries and garden centers for this purpose.

rapid healing from the bark of the trunk itself. A short stub will normally not heal over but gradually dry out and permit the entry of wood-destroying fungi which later weaken the trunk. The pruning of large trees and the repair of extensive storm damage is a job for a professional arborist. Most amateurs have neither the knowledge nor the skill and equipment to clamber safely about the branches of a mature tree.

For home trimming, a good pair of garden shears and a long narrow tree pruning saw which cuts on the draw rather than the push stroke are adequate. The shears will be dull and unsuitable when purchased, and should be sharpened to a razor edge with a fine file and carborundum stone. Sharpen only on the outside of the large flat cutting blade and keep the shears oiled. The "snap cut" type of pruners should not be used because the anvil bruises the branches badly and they are almost impossible to sharpen once they become dull. Cheap shears are an abomination, but a good pair will last a lifetime of ordinary garden use.

Pest and disease control

Articles on pest control often make it seem as though planting a tree is taking on a life of drudgery and unremitting warfare against a horde of invertebrate fiends. In point of fact, trees have withstood insects since time immemorial and would long ago have become extinct had they been unable to do so. Three quarters of the problem is solved by planting a healthy tree in well prepared soil and by fertilizing enough to maintain vigorous growth. Garden birds, and more importantly, predaceous insects maintain ceaseless warfare against the insects which feed on trees. Trees in a vigorous growing condition, aided by the above controls are well equipped for survival.

There is not room in a book of this size for an exhaustive review of the individual insect species which may damage trees. It is better for practical purposes to recognize the symptoms of the three main types of insects which feed on trees and then seek local assistance. If the leaves of a tree become riddled with holes or skeletonized, leaf chewing insects are at work. These may be caterpillars which are the larvae of moths and butterflies or the larvae or adults of leaf eating beetles. If the leaves appear intact but are dull and lifeless-looking with a dusty or stippled surface, sucking insects or mites may be present. These feed on plant juices by sucking them out without consuming the leaf tissue. If holes appear in the branches or trunks of newly planted trees, boring insects, the larvae of certain moths, beetles or wasps, may be present. Such holes frequently show saw dust or sap exuding from them. Where insect damage is suspected, consult the state university or extension entomologist or a local nurseryman or arborist for advice. Most state or provincial universities publish concise bulletins filled with information on safe, effective insect control.

Fungus diseases of trees are far less common than insect pests, and here too maintaining robust good health is the easiest preventative.

133

The imported Dutch elm disease on elms and the imported chestnut blight which wiped out our native American Chestnut are serious exceptions. The former can be avoided by not planting elms where it is present, until some effective solution is found. The latter has exterminated our native chestnut but does not seriously injure the imported Chinese Chestnut. The oak wilt disease which has been known for some time is locally important, but does not give evidence of wide distribution and rapid spread. One of the most common of the fungi affecting trees and shrubs are the powdery mildews which in humid summer weather turn the surfaces of the leaves of some oaks and lilacs, for example, a powdery white color. These are disfiguring rather than lethal diseases, controllable by spraying if desired. A condition which affects street trees in certain years and causes the edges of the leaves to turn brown and dry up is often diagnosed as a fungus disease. Actually it is a physiological leaf scorch caused by hot dry winds which dry up the margins of the leaves faster than the lost water can be replaced by the roots of the trees. It is particularly prevalent in certain tree species such as Sugar Maples and the Katsura Tree especially when they are planted in dry soil locations. Spraying is uneffective and it can be corrected only by supplying additional water in the late spring when the foliage is young and tender. It varies with the weather and may be common one year and entirely absent in subsequent years.

As in the case of insect pests, most trees are well able to live with fungi, and to plant a tree is not to take on an arduous spraying program. Planting as large a variety of tree species as possible enormously reduces the risk that any fungus disease or insect pest can make big inroads into a community's trees. Fungi and most insects are highly specific as to the species they can attack, and only a very few have much catholicity of host acceptance.

An inexpensive tank or knapsack sprayer of 5 gallon capacity is adequate to see young trees or shrubs through their early years. For the home orchard hobbyist, there are small gasoline powered tank sprayers with excellent power and capacity. It is impractical for the home owner to invest in a spraying rig adequate to cover large trees. If needed it is much cheaper and easier to engage the services and knowledge of a professional arborist.

Alphabetical listing of trees described

136

INDEX

Page numbers in **bold face** type indicate color illustrations.

INDEX

Page numbers in **bold face** type indicate color illustrations.

INDEX

Page numbers in **bold face** type indicate color illustrations.

INDEX

Page numbers in **bold face** type indicate color illustrations.

144

156